ALGEBRA FOR ELEMENTARY TEACHERS

1 2 3 4 5 6

HARCOURT, BRACE & WORLD, INC.

New York / Chicago / San Francisco / Atlanta

ALGEBRA
FOR ELEMENTARY TEACHERS

Philip L. Hosford
NEW MEXICO STATE UNIVERSITY

PREFACE

In elementary classrooms today, children are learning the language and symbols of algebra. Concepts such as inside and outside and the relationships of greater than, less than, and equal to, once reserved for advanced study, are now introduced at an early stage. The study of equations is also commonplace. In short, arithmetic no longer adequately describes the content of elementary school programs in mathematics. Only the well-prepared teacher can provide the enriched program the child needs and deserves. It is therefore essential that the elementary teacher have an understanding and appreciation of algebra.

Many excellent high school and college algebra texts are readily available. They are addressed, however, neither to the students preparing to become elementary teachers nor to the elementary teachers wishing to update their knowledge. This book has been written for just such an audience. It is hoped that by using this text the reader will gain an appreciation of the power of generalization found in algebra and will achieve a broader perception of the relationships within the structure of mathematics. He will thus be better prepared to facilitate his students' understanding and the development of their skills.

The selection of topics included in this text meets the spirit of the recommendations set forth for the third course in mathematics (Algebra) by the Committee on the Undergraduate Program in Mathematics of the Mathematical Association of America. The final content of the book, however, was dictated by the experience gained in using the working notes as a text in a course in algebra for the elementary teacher.

An unusual feature of this book is that some of the material is programed. The sections entitled "Check your work on page—" form an integral part in the development of the course. In these sections the student must become involved with the ideas by trying to answer all questions on his own before studying the discussion given in the back of the book. The exercises are not merely restatements of subject matter already discussed; but they ask the student to develop the theory further. Consequently, the student should work most of these problems. A conscious effort has been made to show how every fact, topic, or idea is related to other aspects of mathematics with which the student is already familiar.

Chapter 1 is a brief review of the real numbers. For those students who have not completed a study of the real numbers, this chapter will be more than just a review and should be given considerable attention. In general, it is assumed the student has had at least a year of algebra at the high school level or its equivalent.

Chapter 2 (Linear Equations), Chapter 3 (Quadratics), and Chapter 4 (Systems of Equations) are developmental chapters, necessary to facilitate an understanding of Chapter 5 (The Complex Number System). Graphing is used extensively throughout these chapters to help establish relationships and to provide visual reinforcement for many of the concepts stated. The attitude throughout these chapters is one of seeking a number system that is closed under the operations of addition, multiplication, subtraction, division, and taking the square root. With the accomplishment of this goal in Chapter 5, a major objective of the text is achieved.

Chapter 6 contains interesting and valuable topics usually found in most standard algebra texts, although they are not a necessary part of the development in Chapters 1–5. Some instructors may feel that these topics are essential and will wish to introduce them at particular stages to help in the development of various concepts.

I wish to express my gratitude to the many students, mathematicians, and educators who contributed constructive criticism, advice, and encouragement. I am particularly indebted to: Professor Fred Richman, Palma Ross, Neal Hart, and Ray Graham for their careful reading of the working notes of the text; to the students who used the text during the two semesters of 1966–67, for their invaluable suggestions; and to Janelle Quesenberry, Bobby Bailey, and Emmitt Champion, three senior mathematics majors, for checking every exercise and for their many helpful suggestions.

PHILIP L. HOSFORD

CONTENTS

3 QUADRATIC EQUATIONS   65

4 SYSTEMS OF EQUATIONS
AND INEQUALITIES   118

GLOSSARY OF SYMBOLS

General

$\Leftrightarrow$	If and only if
$\Rightarrow$	Implies that
$= (\neq)$	Equals (does not equal)
$< (>)$	Less than (greater than)
$\leqq (\geqq)$	Less than or equal to (greater than or equal to)
$\equiv$	Congruent to, or identical to
$\left.\begin{array}{c} \oplus \\ \otimes \\ \# \\ * \end{array}\right\}$	Operational symbols for fields
$\cdots$	Ellipsis, indicates missing terms
RST	Reflexive, symmetric, transitive properties

Numbers

0	Zero (additive identity)
1	One (multiplicative identity)
i	$\sqrt{-1}$, imaginary number
$a + bi$	Complex number
$a - bi$	Complex conjugate of $a + bi$
$n!$	n factorial
$|a|$	Absolute value of a
$1.\overline{234}$	Repeating decimal

Sets

A, S	Sets
$\in (\notin)$	Is (is not) an element of
$S = \{a, b, x\}$	The elements of the set S are a, b, and x
$S = \{x \mid x \in S\}$	The set S consists of all x satisfying the condition $x \in S$
$N(S)$	Number of elements of the set S
$A \subset B \ (A \not\subset B)$	The set A is (is not) contained in the set B
$A \cup B$	The union of set A and set B
$A \cap B$	The intersection of set A and set B
U	Universe, the largest set under consideration
A'	Complement of set A
$\{\ \}$ or $\varnothing$	Empty set or set with no elements
C	Counting numbers
W	Whole numbers
I	Integers
Ra	Rational numbers
Irr	Irrational numbers
R	Real numbers
$C^{\#}$	Complex numbers
$X \times Y$	Cartesian Product

Functions

$f(x), G(x), h(x)$	f, G, h are functions
D	Domain
R	Range

ALGEBRA FOR ELEMENTARY TEACHERS

INTRODUCTION: The Philosophy of Modern Mathematics

When we speak of the philosophy of modern mathematics we are referring to those principles which form the rational foundation of modern mathematics. The same kind of phrase is used when we speak of the philosophy of education, the philosophy of teaching, or the philosophy of government. In the elementary school, the philosophy of modern mathematics rests on the assumption that an appreciation of the structure of mathematics together with an understanding of the processes of mathematics will lead students to greater achievement.

Mathematics is a man-made *single* structure. Its construction was motivated by the most practical reasons. It had its origin in sheer necessity, beginning with the need for a concept of number. The idea of naming a given set of things came slowly. Philosophers believe that even the concepts of "twoness" or "threeness" were major breakthroughs. Two of anything, that is, not just the naming of a set of two boys, two chickens, or two rocks, but just *two*. We can discover signs of failure in mastering this concept by examining some contemporary languages. We find the problem in our own language in words like brace, pair, team, and couple. In many primitive languages today, words for one and two are found, but for any larger quantity only a word such as "heap" (or some other word meaning "a bunch") is discovered.

On this foundation of the concept of number, man began building. For untold years he counted on his fingers and then set aside a rock to represent two full hands of fingers (as shepherds did in counting their sheep returning from pasture). At other times he may have tied a knot in a string for each ten sheep as they went to pasture, and then he untied the knot upon the return of each group of ten. For how many years this went on before someone perceived that he could indicate the number of tens by writing the number in a special way, no one knows. But whenever this did occur, the two cornerstones of our mathematical structure were laid—the invention of numerals and the concept of place value. Thousands of years later, the system of rational numbers with the many algorithms we teach boys and girls in school today was finally completed.

Our basic assumption in teaching mathematics involves accurate understanding of the processes of mathematics as well as an appreciation of its structure. In the past we have too often been satisfied with shallow understanding. For too long we have taught the tricks and rules without rational explanation. If a student wanted to know why he had to "turn it up-side-down and multiply," we told him he did it because that was the way to do it.

Contemporary mathematics teaching demands better understanding by the student. Learning is not a mere accumulation of knowledge, but is a process of growth. The child learns nothing from words that are divorced from meaning. Too many pupils finish school hating mathematics because they learned only words. If we continue to teach the same way we taught in the past, we will achieve the same unsatisfactory results with modern mathematics. We can teach first graders to recite in set language and invoke the commutative and associative laws. But as the years go by the children will realize they learned only words—not ideas. They will know that a parrot could recite the words as they do. They will suspect that they do not deserve their A grades. And because they fear being discovered in this fraud, they will come to hate mathematics itself as the apparent cause of their lack of understanding.

To gain an appreciation and understanding of the structure of mathematics, we must have improvement in instruction. Today, we know much about a student's readiness, particularly in regard to the teaching of reading. We may sometimes use the lack of "readiness" as an excuse for doing little about it. We could make the same error in mathematics. We should not teach a child material for which he is not ready—that is true. But it does not follow that we should wait until the child is ready. With some children we could wait for years! Obviously, instead of waiting passively, we should actively help the child to become ready. If a child is not ready to learn the commutative property of addition, we should not try to teach it. Rather, we should give the child concrete objects to maneuver. We should ask him questions about sums which he can successfully answer. We should work at preparing him to discover the property for himself.

Modern mathematics teaching recognizes the concept of individual differences, including differences in groups of children and in classroom readiness. Today, for example, a second grade child might say something about infinity. If asked what infinity means, he might announce that infinity is "after a million or something." Unexpectedly the class is ready for a discussion of the concept of infinity, and the teacher should be able to capitalize on that readiness.

Mental growth is encouraged by the experience of seeing things from many different angles, in many different ways, through many different eyes.

The truly fine teacher who understands this can hasten his students' mental growth. This means there is no longer just one way to do mathematics; just one way to do a problem; just one way to compute. But if only one way of computation is selected and demanded of the students, the teacher should explain the arbitrariness of his decision and give the students reasons for it. Yes, even if the method was selected to make paper grading easier or because future learning will be speeded if all use the same algorithm, the students should be shown that we are arbitrary and they will understand. Furthermore, they will have achieved greater understanding of the structure of mathematics.

Part of the improvement in learning will come from better evaluation. The teaching of modern mathematics demands better evaluation. We no longer evaluate a child in reading by saying he is a 4-2 level reader. We talk instead of the child's visual perception, his reading vocabulary, his speed, his comprehension, his word analysis skills. Similarly, there is no typical fifth grade mathematics student today. "Johnnie is strong on his basic multiplication facts, weak in spatial perceptions, 'O.K.' in place value, needs more work in inductive thinking, is surprisingly strong in deductive thinking, especially in unraveling word problems." Now we have evaluated the student and we have communicated something.

Finally, better learning results from the integrated nature of modern mathematics programs. Mathematics should no longer be taught as an isolated subject, which is unrelated to even last year's work. Algebra should not be a "new subject," but a logical extension of principles learned in arithmetic. Teaching mathematics as an isolated subject, compartmentalized into disjoint subsets of rules and tricks is the very antithesis of the philosophy of modern mathematics. Mathematics can and must be related to other parts of itself, to other subjects in the curriculum, and to real life problems. The ideas underlying all concepts such as function, variable, and distributivity are all interrelated.

Educators tell us that the best motivation for learning is learning itself. The philosophy of modern mathematics leans heavily on that premise.

Set Language and Operations

The Counting Numbers

The Closure Property

The Rational Numbers

Decimal Notation

Repeating Decimals

Irrational Numbers

The RST Properties

The Real Number System

1

THE REAL NUMBERS

We begin our study of algebra and its place in the structure of mathematics with a brief review of the real number system and the vocabulary, symbols, and basic concepts that we will use throughout this text. The real numbers and their properties provide us with many of the basic tools for our study of algebra.

Some of you may have completed a study of the real number system on the college level. All of you studied the rational numbers in elementary school and the real numbers in secondary school. A review of the real numbers in this first chapter should help us all attain a common ground regarding language, symbols, and definitions. As you progress through the text always study carefully the sections headed "Checking Your Work" found at the end of each chapter; these are important self-teaching sections of the text.

1.1   Set Language and Operations

Any formal presentation of the real number system is greatly facilitated by the use of set language. Some of the concepts and much of the language of sets should therefore be at your command. Before we begin this section, let us determine just how much you know or can figure out for yourself about set language and the associated operations. If the notation is new to you, or difficult to recall, study the Glossary of Symbols on page xiii.

5

We often need to find the *intersection* ∩ and the *union* ∪ of various pairs of sets, and also the *complement* of each of them.

Suppose you are given the sets A, B, C, and D in the *universe U* of *integers I*. That is, if $U = I$ (all positive and negative whole numbers and zero), consider the sets:

$$A = \{-2, -1, 0, 1, 2\} \qquad C = \{x \mid x < 3\}$$
$$B = \{-2, 0\} \qquad D = \{x \mid x \geq 3\}$$

Try the following exercises.

1. Find:

   a. $A \cap B$ c. $A \cap D$

   b. $A \cap C$ d. $C \cup D$

2. List all pairs of sets that are *disjoint*.

3. What is the complement of C?

Now that you have tried, see how well you did, and

CHECK YOUR WORK on page 32

Did you find the correct answers to all questions? If not, you will want to study the following presentation with care.

Set Language

Set
A set can be

any group of objects

living creatures

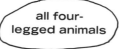
all four-legged animals

or ideas

rules for chess

Element

An element is a member of a set. If A is the set whose elements are 1, 2, and 3, we record this fact as $A = \{1, 2, 3\}$. Then 2 is an element of set A, and we write $2 \in A$. The symbol $\in$ is read "is an element (or member) of." Since 5 is not an element of A, we write $5 \notin A$, where $\notin$ is read "is not a member of."

Subset

A subset is a set that is contained in another set. A is a subset of B if every element of A is a member of B. If

$$A = \{1, 2, 3\}, \qquad B = \{1, 2, 3, 4, 5, 6\}, \qquad \text{and} \qquad H = \{3, 4, 5\}$$

then, since every element of A is contained in B, we say "A is a subset of B" and denote this by writing $A \subset B$. Similarly, $H \subset B$. But every element of H is not contained in A, so we know that H is not a subset of A and write this as $H \not\subset A$. Is $A \subset A$? Yes, because every element of A is contained in A.

Empty Set

The empty set is the set having no elements. This set is also called the *null* set and is written as $\{\ \}$ or $\varnothing$.

Universe

The universe is the set containing all possible members under consideration. If the universe U is the set of counting numbers C, then the set A given above is a subset of U. However, if the universe is defined as the set of all odd counting numbers, then $A \not\subset U$, because the element "2" is an element of A and is not contained in U.

Disjoint Sets

Disjoint sets are sets having no elements in common. If $A = \{1, 2, 3\}$ and $K = \{5, 6\}$, then A and K are disjoint sets. The set of all dogs and the set of all cats are disjoint.

Complement

The complement of a set is that part of the universe which is not contained in the set. If S is the set of all counting numbers greater than 4, the complement of S within the universe of counting numbers is the set $S' = \{1, 2, 3\}$. If the universe is given as $\{7, 8, 9\}$, then the complement of $\{8\}$ is $\{7, 9\}$. The prime indicates the complement of a set; the set M' (read "M prime") is the complement of the set M.

Set Form

Sets are usually shown either in descriptive or in tabular (roster) form. The tabular form usually shows each element of the set. For example, the set $A = \{1, 2, 3\}$. In descriptive form, we can write for A

$$A = \{x | x < 4\} \quad \text{where } U = C$$

and we read this as "A is the set of all elements x such that x is less than four, and the universe is the set of all counting numbers."

Operations

Intersection of Sets

The intersection of two or more sets is the set of all elements common to the sets considered. For the sets $H = \{3, 4, 5\}$ and $K = \{5, 6\}$, the element 5 is the common element; thus, the intersection of H and K is $\{5\}$. This is expressed as $H \cap K = \{5\}$. Also, for $A = \{1, 2, 3\}$, we see that $K \cap A = \{\ \}$.

Union

The union of two or more sets is the set of all elements that belong to at least one of the sets in question; thus, for H and K defined as above the union of H and K is $\{3, 4, 5, 6\}$. We show this union as $H \cup K = \{3, 4, 5, 6\}$, and say "the union of H and K is the set whose members are 3, 4, 5, and 6." Similarly, {Bill, Jack, Jane} $\cup$ {Jack, Dick, Jane} = {Bill, Jack, Jane, Dick}.

Although the elements of a set are usually written in some order, this is not a requirement. The set $\{1, 2, 3\}$ could just as well be written $\{2, 1, 3\}$. Another cause for occasional confusion is the multiple listing of the same element in a set. That is, are the sets $\{1, 1, 2, 3\}$ and $\{1, 2, 3\}$ equivalent? The answer, of course, is yes. The number 1 is an element of the set regardless of how often it is listed. In the case of {Bill, Tom, Harry, Harry}, however, we would have to be sure that Harry refers to the same person both times.

EXERCISES
1.1

1. Given:

$$A = \{0, 1, 2\} \qquad C = \{5, 6\}$$
$$B = \{0, 3, 4, 5\} \qquad D = \{2\}$$

Find:

a. $A \cap D$ e. $A \cup D$

b. $A \cap C$ f. $C \cup D$

c. $A \cap B$ g. $(A \cap C) \cup B$

d. $A \cup C$ h. $(A \cap C) \cap B$

2. If $E = \{x|x < 2\}$ and $U = C$

     a. Write E in tabular form.

     b. Write the complement of E.

3. For the five sets in problems 1 and 2 list all the pairs of sets that are disjoint.

4. Regardless of the elements contained in sets F and G, what will be their intersection if:

     a. $F \subset G$

     b. F is the complement of G

     c. G is the empty set

5. Given $S = \{0, 1, 2, 3, 4, 5, 6, 7, 8, 9\}$. Find a subset of S whose elements are equal to the sum of 3 and twice an element of S (write in tabular form).

1.2   The Counting Numbers

Most studies of the real number system begin with an examination of the counting numbers. One should try to acquire an appreciation for the magnificent development of our Hindu-Arabic method of numeration. Our system of numeration as we know and use it today was not completed until the early 1600's. Centuries were needed for the Hindus to develop just the symbols for the digits. The use of zero as a digit, the idea of place value, and the development of our algorism added still more centuries to the completion of this great invention.

In most texts, and in particular, in most elementary school texts, the counting numbers are defined such that zero is not included, probably because when one starts counting objects one begins one's counting with one. Not including zero as a counting number is also in harmony with standard treatment. Therefore, in this text, the counting numbers are defined as

$C = \{1, 2, 3, 4, \ldots\}$

And the set of counting numbers plus zero are defined as

$W = \{0, 1, 2, 3, \ldots\}$

In some texts, however, the number "zero" is included in the set of counting numbers because it counts the number of elements in the empty set or the number of elements in the intersection of disjoint sets. If $S = \{0\}$, or $\{1\}$, or $\{4\}$, the number of elements in S is 1. Another way of saying this is $N(S) = 1$. But if $S = \{\}$ or $\emptyset$, then the number of elements in S is 0, or $N(S) = 0$.

You may recall from your earlier work in mathematics that the binary operations of addition and multiplication of counting numbers satisfy the *associative* and *commutative* properties. Can you give numerical examples of these two properties? Better still—can you give definitions for them? Try, and then

CHECK YOUR WORK on page 33

The *distributive* property of multiplication over addition in C also holds. Can you make up two or three numerical examples illustrating the distributive property similar to the following one?

$$2(3 + 4) = (2 \cdot 3) + (2 \cdot 4)$$
$$2 \cdot (7) = \quad (6) + (8)$$
$$14 = 14$$

In general, the *distributive property* provides that if a, b, $c \in C$, then

$$a(b + c) = a \cdot b + a \cdot c$$

EXERCISES
1.2

For $U = C$, give a numerical example illustrating the following properties.

1. Distributive property of multiplication over addition.
2. Associative property of addition.
3. Commutative property of addition.
4. Associative property of multiplication.
5. Commutative property of multiplication.

Name the property that justifies each of the following equations.

6. $3(4 + 1) = 3 \cdot 4 + 3 \cdot 1$
7. $98 + 37 + 2 = 98 + 2 + 37$
8. $98 + 2 + 37 = (98 + 2) + 37$
9. $(3 + 2)(4 + 5) = (3 + 2)4 + (3 + 2)5$

1.3   The Closure Property

Another important attribute of the set of counting numbers under the two operations of addition and multiplication is the property of *closure* — an idea that students sometimes fail to appreciate, possibly because they become lost in unraveling the language often used to define it. Let us state the property of closure in more ordinary language to see if this might help.

When we find the sum or product of two numbers we want to get an answer that is meaningful to us, that is, *an answer which is in our universe.* Let us examine a case that does not have closure and see if this will explain the meaning of the concept. Assume that you are an intelligent sort of caveman and have for some time been counting up to ten on your fingers, and that you have gone further to conceptualize the fact that $3 + 4 = 7$, let us see what you might do with the concept of closure. Your universe is the set of numerals that we commonly label $\{1, 2, 3, 4, 5, 6, 7, 8, 9, 10\}$. Now, suppose you tax your mental prowess by wondering what $7 + 8$ would be. Remembering to constrain yourself to the limitations of a caveman and his universe of numbers (your ten fingers), you realize that the answer to $7 + 8$ is something outside of your range of perception — something outside your universe of numerals as well as your concept of number.

Stated in our set language, the set $S = \{1, 2, 3, 4, 5, 6, 7, 8, 9, 10\}$ is not closed with respect to the operation of addition, because not all sums obtained by adding two elements of the set are themselves members of the set. For example, $7 + 8 = 15$, but 15 is not an element of S.

To conclude this discussion in more formal mathematical language, closure is obtained when a given operation on a given set yields an element *of the given set.* We therefore say the set is closed with respect to, or under, the operation. For example, on the set of counting numbers, the binary operation of addition yields another counting number; therefore, the set C is closed under the operation of addition.

The desire for closure under all operations motivates an expansion of the set of counting numbers to include the set of integers I. Obviously, the subtraction of 8 from 5 yields something that is outside the set of counting numbers. To achieve closure, we must therefore enlarge our set. Even with the operation of addition, when faced with the unfinished statement $8 + x = 5$, we can find no replacement for x within our universe, and we again are frustrated.

Happily, we find that the expansion of the set to include all the negative integers does not upset the associative, commutative, and distributive properties. As a matter of fact, we gain the additive inverse, which provides for every $a \in I$, the existence of $-a$ (read "negative a") such that

$$a + (-a) = 0$$

Thus, we have achieved closure under the operation of subtraction.

The desire for closure under division prompts a further expansion of our concepts and of the set of symbols in our number system because in I we fail to find nonempty solution sets to statements such as: $2x = 7$ and $13y = 3$. The result is the set of rational numbers Ra. And again we have gained. This time we have obtained the multiplicative inverse, which provides closure under the operation of division except by zero (and provides the basis for the familiar rule of "invert and multiply").

To show whether or not you fully grasp the meaning of closure, see how successful you are with the following three problems.

1. Given that the set of counting numbers is closed under the operation of multiplication, show that the set of *even* counting numbers is either closed or not closed under multiplication, and explain your answer.

2. Given the set of odd counting numbers, is the set closed under the operation of addition? Why?

3. Define a set, not yet discussed, and an operation such that this set is not closed under the given operation because the result of the operation is not contained in the set.

Before checking your work on these exercises, you will do well to spend as much time thinking about them and working at them as if you had been assigned a full page of exercises. Do not become alarmed if you do not find a satisfactory answer at first glance. As a last resort, or only after you know you have done the assignment correctly,

CHECK YOUR WORK on page 33

EXERCISES
1.3

1. Is the set $\{2, 4, 6, 8\}$ closed under addition? Explain your answer.

2. Is the set of odd counting numbers closed under multiplication?

3. Consider the set $\{0, 1\}$ and the four fundamental operations of addition, subtraction, multiplication, and division. Discuss the closure property with respect to this set and each of the operations.

4. Define the smallest set of counting numbers you can think of that will be closed under addition.

5. Define the smallest possible set of integers that will be closed under addition.

1.4 The Rational Numbers

The set of rational numbers Ra was developed so that we could obtain closure with respect to the operation of division and is commonly defined as

$$Ra = \left\{ \frac{a}{b} \middle| a, b \in I, b \neq 0 \right\}$$

Stated in words, "the set of rational numbers is the set of all ordered pairs of integers, the second not being zero and each pair representing a fraction."

The multiplicative inverse gained by the expansion to Ra provides that for every $a \in Ra$ $(a \neq 0)$ there exists an element $1/a$, such that

$$a \cdot \frac{1}{a} = 1$$

By using this property, we can now find a satisfactory replacement for x in an equation such as

$\frac{3}{7}x = \frac{5}{6}$

Multiplying both members of the equation by $\frac{7}{3}$ (the multiplicative inverse, or reciprocal, of $\frac{3}{7}$), we obtain

$\frac{7}{3} \cdot \frac{3}{7}x = \frac{7}{3} \cdot \frac{5}{6}$

or

$x = \frac{35}{18}$

Since the rationals are closed under multiplication, we need only define division in terms of multiplication to show closure with respect to division. Division can be defined in terms of multiplication and the preceding example as follows:

$\frac{5}{6} \div \frac{3}{7} = x \iff \frac{3}{7} \cdot x = \frac{5}{6}$

The double-headed arrow indicates that the expression to the left is true if and only if the expression to the right is true. (See Glossary of Symbols.)

In general terms, we can say

$$\frac{a}{b} \div \frac{c}{d} = \frac{h}{f} \iff \frac{c}{d} \cdot \frac{h}{f} = \frac{a}{b}$$

where a/b, c/d, $h/f \in Ra$ and $c/d \neq 0$.

Among the number systems we have so far discussed, the rational numbers form the first set that is closed under all four of the basic operations of arithmetic—addition, subtraction, multiplication, and division (except by zero). It is not surprising then that dealing with the rational number system provides the major subject matter of the elementary-school mathematics curriculum. Mastery of the rational numbers is a primary objective of the elementary school program. Throughout the remainder of this textbook we will be using the operations and properties of the rational number system.

Check your ability in computing with the rational numbers by doing the following exercises.

EXERCISES
1.4

Simplify the following expressions.

1. $\frac{2}{3} + \frac{3}{4} + \frac{1}{2}$ 3. $\frac{3}{2} - \frac{4}{7}$

2. $\dfrac{3}{4} \div \dfrac{5}{2}$ 4. $6 - \dfrac{12}{5}$

5. $(\frac{2}{3} + \frac{5}{6}) \div \frac{17}{12}$

6. $\dfrac{-5(3 - x) - 3(x - 5)}{2a + 1 - 2a}$

7. $-\frac{2}{3}(\frac{1}{4} + \frac{3}{2})$

8. $\dfrac{5 + \frac{1}{3}}{5 - \frac{1}{3}}$

1.5 Decimal Notation

The need to obtain closure under division within the set of nonnegative rational numbers emphasized the usefulness of our decimal notation. It is puzzling that the Greeks or the Hindus did not invent decimal notation; it seems such an obvious extension to us today.

Why must place value indication stop at the unit's place? Why not extend place value to the right as well? All we would need to do this is some sort of reference point to indicate the unit's position, and all other place values to the right would then follow. Such a reference point might have been a dash, 284-679; or a slash bar, 284/679; or an asterisk, 284*679; or, as it has turned out to be, a simple period, 284.679. In Germany the *comma* is used instead of the period, and the period is used where we use the comma. Hence, 48.002,67 is read "forty-eight thousand two and sixty-seven hundredths."

When we expand a numeral to illustrate place value as in

$$65{,}284 = 6(10{,}000) + 5(1000) + 2(100) + 8(10) + 4(1)$$

the simplicity of the concept is striking. A numeral could be expanded by simply viewing each succeeding place value as being 1/10th of the previous one so that, for example,

$$284.679 = 2(100) + 8(10) + 4(1) + 6(\tfrac{1}{10}) + (\tfrac{1}{100}) + 9(\tfrac{1}{1000})$$

This number is read directly from the expanded form as "2 hundreds, 8 tens, 4 ones, 6 tenths, 7 one-hundredths, and 9 one-thousandths," or "two hundred eighty-four and six hundred seventy-nine thousandths." In this way the idea of expanding the place values to the right is implemented with a dot placed after the unit's digit, with the dot being read "and."

We capitalize on this development in our numeration system every time we speak in terms of money. When we say forty-eight dollars and fifty-eight cents and write $48.58, we are extending the place value idea to include dimes and pennies, which correspond to tenths and hundredths of a unit (the dollar).

The invention of the decimal notation also permitted the development and application of the common division algorithm using decimal points which are especially helpful when the divisor is larger than the dividend. If $\frac{5}{8}$ is viewed as a problem in division without decimal notation, we simply say there are no "groups of 8" in 5. Or, using the division algorithm for a/b, $a = bq + r$ (where $b \neq 0$, $0 \leq r < b$), we find that $5 = 8q + r$; or $5 = 8(0) + 5$. But with decimal notation we can rewrite the problem as $5.000 \div 8$ and find the quotient 0.625. In terms of $a = bq + r$ we now have $5.000 = 8(0.625) + 0$ and we can say 8 divides 5.000 exactly in Ra.

To continue our review of the real numbers, we recall that every element of the set of rational numbers can be expressed by an equivalent decimal fraction, either terminating or repeating. Or, in other words, we know that any nonzero integer will divide another integer either exactly or in such a way that a block of the digits in the dividend will begin repeating a definite series. Terminating decimals are often treated as a subset of the set of repeating decimals, since in the terminating decimal the digit zero repeats itself. An example of a repeating decimal is the decimal form of the rational number $\frac{1}{3}$ which is 0.33333 . . . . In this case, the digit 3 repeats itself. Similarly, the rational number $\frac{1}{2}$ can be written as 0.5000 . . . , and in this form it is a repeating decimal. Of course, we ordinarily do not write the zeros, and we call 0.5 a terminating decimal.

In the standard notation of repeating decimals such a decimal as 0.333333 . . . is commonly written as $0.\overline{3}$, where the bar above the 3 indicates that the 3 is repeated indefinitely. The numeral 1.123535353535 . . . is written as $1.12\overline{35}$ indicating that the block of digits 35 is repeated indefinitely. The repeating part of a decimal is called the *repetend*.

You would do well to convince yourself of the truth of the statement that all rational numbers are members of the set of repeating decimals. Do this by converting the following rational numbers to decimal equivalents:

1. $\frac{1}{7}$ 3. $\frac{11}{12}$
2. $\frac{5}{9}$ 4. $\frac{27}{40}$

5. Now develop a logical statement or proof that all rational numbers are members of the set of repeating decimals.

Carefully consider your answer to question 5, and then

CHECK YOUR WORK on page 34

1.6   Repeating Decimals

Now that we have established the fact that all rational numbers can be expressed as repeating decimals, we might reasonably hope that all repeating decimals can be expressed as rational numbers. Even though this idea is not new to you, do you believe it? *Every repeating decimal can be expressed in the form of a fraction comprised of two integers.* Are you convinced that a decimal such as $0.\overline{538461}$ is equal to some rational number? Is it possible then to find that rational number?

It is, and we shall find it, but first let us review the procedure with a simpler decimal. Let us find the rational number that is equal to $0.\overline{36}$.

Is there some number, other than itself, from which we might subtract $0.\overline{36}$ and obtain a difference that is an element of the set of integers? Suppose you want to subtract $0.\overline{36}$ from $5.\overline{36}$. Don't read further—try it.

What did you obtain? Let us write the problem as follows:

$$5.36363636363636\ldots$$
$$-0.36363636363636\ldots$$
$$\overline{5.00000000000000\ldots}$$

We see that correct answers include 5, 5.000 . . . , or $5.\overline{0}$, which are all names for the same number. We now have to find an a and b such that $a/b = 0.\overline{36}$. Suppose we multiply both sides of this equation by 100 and obtain $100\dfrac{a}{b} = 36.\overline{36}$. If we now subtract as follows

$$100\frac{a}{b} = 36.\overline{36}$$
$$- \quad \frac{a}{b} = -\ 0.\overline{36}$$
$$\overline{99\frac{a}{b} = 36.\overline{0}} \quad \text{or} \quad \frac{a}{b} = \frac{36}{99}$$

We obtain 36/99, which is a rational number! Of course the result should be reduced to lowest terms by dividing out the common factors. Thus,

$$\frac{36}{99} = \frac{\cancel{3} \cdot \cancel{3} \cdot 4}{\cancel{3} \cdot \cancel{3} \cdot 11} = \frac{4}{11}$$
$$0.36 = \frac{4}{11}$$

Let us now apply the same method to $0.\overline{538461}$. To successfully align the repeating series so that the differences obtained to the right of the decimal point will all be zero, we must multiply our number by 1,000,000. We then have

$$538,461.\overline{538461} = 1,000,000N$$
$$- \quad 0.\overline{538461} = - \quad N$$
$$\overline{538,461.000000 = 999,999N}$$

$$\left(N = \frac{a}{b}; \ a, b \in I \text{ and } b \neq 0\right)$$

Dividing both sides of the equation by 999,999, we obtain

$$N = \frac{538,461}{999,999}$$

which is, indeed, a rational number. In its simplest form this number is $\frac{7}{13}$.

What if the decimal does not begin repeating promptly after the decimal point, as, for example, in 2.23616161 ... ? In this case we first multiply the number by a power of ten to locate the repeating part of the decimal immediately following the decimal point. That is, we multiply N by 100 so that $100N = 223.616161$ .... Continuing as before, we subtract

$$10,000N = 22,361.616161 \ldots$$
$$- \quad 100N = \quad 223.616161 \ldots$$
$$\overline{9,900N = 22,138.000000 \ldots}$$

and, finally,

$$N = \frac{22,138}{9900} = \frac{11,069}{4950}$$

The serious student will want to check this answer by dividing 11,069 by 4950 to see if we really do obtain $2.23\overline{61}$.

Before you try some of these conversions, let us recall the definition of prime numbers, so you can use them to reduce fractions; that is, to determine if 11,069/4950 is really "reduced" as far as possible.

A prime number is an integer greater than 1 that has no positive integral factors except itself and 1. In dealing with such a number as 538,461/999,999, it is often profitable to factor the numerator and the denominator in performing the reduction process to help determine if you have reached the simplest representative of the class (that is, reduced the fraction to its lowest terms). If you held a position where all you did all day was factor such numbers, it would be worthwhile to develop an algorithm to help you if you could not get a suitable machine! In factoring numbers, one helpful procedure is to extract prime factors until the number is reduced to a prime. The last prime together with those extracted then comprise the factors of the number. For example, we can find the prime factorization of 60 as follows:

$$
\begin{array}{r}
5 \\
3\overline{)15} \\
2\overline{)30} \\
2\overline{)60}
\end{array}
$$

Therefore the prime factorization of 60 is $2 \cdot 2 \cdot 3 \cdot 5 = 60$.

Similarly, to reduce the fraction 528,461/999,999 we first obtain

$$
\begin{array}{r}
37 \\
11\overline{)407} \\
7\overline{)2849} \\
7\overline{)19943} \\
3\overline{)59829} \\
3\overline{)179487} \\
3\overline{)538461}
\end{array}
\qquad \text{and} \qquad
\begin{array}{r}
37 \\
13\overline{)481} \\
7\overline{)3367} \\
3\overline{)10101} \\
11\overline{)111111} \\
3\overline{)333333} \\
3\overline{)999999}
\end{array}
$$

Now we note that

$$
\frac{538,461}{999,999} = \frac{3 \cdot 3 \cdot 3 \cdot 7 \cdot 7 \cdot 11 \cdot 37}{3 \cdot 3 \cdot 3 \cdot 7 \cdot 11 \cdot 13 \cdot 37}
$$

After dividing out like factors in the numerator and denominator we obtain $\frac{7}{13}$.

Is 11,069/4950 the simplest representative of its class? When you are convinced that you have the answer and can defend it,

CHECK YOUR WORK on page 35

EXERCISES
1.6

Find the rational number in reduced form that is equal to:

1. $0.\overline{7}$
2. $0.\overline{4}$
3. $0.2\overline{5}$
4. $0.\overline{36}$
5. $0.91\overline{6}$
6. $0.\overline{211}$
7. $0.375\overline{0}$
8. $0.\overline{123}$
9. $0.4\overline{123}$
10. $0.\overline{285714}$

11. Compare your answer to problem 10 with the answer to problem 1 on page 16. What can you conclude?

12. Develop a general formula for converting any repeating decimal to its fractional equivalent. Begin by labeling the general decimal fraction as

$$N = 0.a_1a_2a_3 \cdots a_n\overline{a_{n+1} \cdots a_m}$$

(where a_{n+1} is the first digit of the repetend, each a, n, m represent nonnegative integers, and the subscripts indicate the ordered position to the right of the decimal point).

1.7   Irrational Numbers

The set of rational numbers has the property referred to as *denseness*. That is, the rational numbers are so numerous that between any two numbers there can be found a third number, no matter how close to each other the first two numbers may be. This idea will be obvious when you realize that given any two rational numbers their average will be a rational number exactly halfway between them.

The existence of such a rational number depends on closure under the operations necessary to find an average. When we seek the average of two rational numbers, we first add the two numbers. Their sum is rational because of closure under addition. We then divide this sum by 2, or multiply it by the rational number $\frac{1}{2}$; since the rationals are closed under both of these operations, we again obtain a rational number.

The concept of denseness often leads the student to believe that the number line has finally been filled by the rational numbers. That is, each point on the line has a name that is associated with a rational number. This, however, is not true. An immense number of "holes" can still be found on the number line. As a matter of fact, we know that for every point on the number line associated with a rational number there are an infinite number of points on the number line that do not correspond to a rational number.

The correspondence of points on the number line with numbers is completed by the union of *Ra* with the set of *irrational numbers Irr*. With the sets *Ra* and *Irr* at our command, we can now associate every point on the number line with a number, thus "plugging all the holes." The union of these two sets is thus the set of *real numbers,*

$$R = Ra \cup Irr$$

Perhaps the best way to find out what the irrational numbers are is to consider what we know they are not. We know they cannot be expressed as repeating decimals or then they would be rationals. Likewise, we know they cannot be expressed as one integer divided by another (with the denominator not zero).

We could say, however, that the irrational numbers are those represented by nonrepeating decimals. Are there such numbers? Consider the decimal

0.123456789101112131415161718192021222324252627282 9 . . .

We can continue writing this decimal forever without establishing a repetend. Let us write another:

0.102003000400005000006000000700000008 . . .

and so on indefinitely, writing first a positive integer and then a number of zeros equal to the preceding integer.

But where do such numbers come from? Do they not appear meaningless? Would we ever have use for them? It turns out that they are very necessary and have other representations, which we will recognize.

In the past others have also been puzzled by the existence of the irrational numbers. The Greeks, and in particular the Pythagoreans, knew of such numbers and were so dismayed by the discovery of these "incommensurables" that they viewed them as unutterable and formless aspects of some other life. All members of the Pythagorean Society were sworn to secrecy regarding the very existence of such numbers; there are stories about members being assassinated for divulging the existence of such mysterious numbers, while others perished at sea for failing to conceal such "incommensurables." [1]

All of this controversy arose from the discovery of lines that could not be measured. For example, recall the Pythagorean theorem, which states that the square of the hypotenuse of a right triangle is equal to the sum of the squares of the other two sides. In the particular case of a triangle of sides 3 and 4 and hypotenuse 5, all was well because $3^2 + 4^2 = 9 + 16 = 25 = 5^2$.

However, in the case of the triangle with sides 1 and 1, the hypotenuse cannot be expressed as a rational number. Consider $1^2 + 1^2 = 1 + 1 = 2$. The problem of $2 = a^2$ lead to the search for a number such that $a \cdot a = 2$. Because the rational numbers are closed under multiplication, one might expect that if a rational number is the product

---

[1] For an interesting discussion of "forbidden mathematics," see Edna E. Kramer, *The Main Stream of Mathematics* (New York City: Oxford University Press, Inc., 1951). (In paperback—New York City: Premier Books, Fawcett World Library, 1961.)

of two numbers (even if they are equal), then the two numbers are rational numbers themselves. Specifically, if $a^2 = 2$, then $a \cdot a = 2$; and intuitively, we might expect that the square root of 2 would therefore be a rational number.

Let us assume that the square root of 2 is a rational number, the simplest representative of its class (reduced). If $a^2 = 2$, then $a = \sqrt{2}$, and a can be written as one integer over another

$$a = \frac{b}{c} \qquad \text{where } c \neq 0$$

and b, c have no common factors, that is, they are *relatively prime*. Since $a^2 = 2$, then

$$\frac{b^2}{c^2} = 2 \qquad \text{or} \qquad \frac{b}{c} \cdot \frac{b}{c} = 2$$

Multiplying both sides of this equation by c^2, we obtain $b^2 = 2c^2$, which means that b^2 has a factor of 2 and is therefore an even number. But if b^2 has a factor of 2, then b itself must have a factor of 2, and b must be an even number. This fact can be stated as $b = 2k$, where k is any integer.

Since $b = 2k$, then $b^2 = 4k^2$. But $b^2 = 2c^2$, so that $4k^2 = 2c^2$. Dividing this last equation by 2, we find $2k^2 = c^2$, which means that c^2 is an even number and has a factor of 2. But if c^2 has a factor of 2, then so must c; hence c itself is even. We have shown both b and c to be even numbers, which means that the fraction b/c can be reduced by dividing the numerator and denominator by 2. This is a contradiction of our original assumption of b/c being relatively prime (reduced). Therefore the statement that $b/c = a$ is a rational number is false, and the number a must be irrational.

We have given several decimals that are irrational numbers and have proved that $\sqrt{2}$ is irrational. The Greeks found still another such number that was very useful. They noted that the circumference of a circle was always very close numerically to the length of three of its diameters. When they took a piece of string the length of a circle's diameter and laid it out along the circumference of the circle, the circumference was always found to be a little more than three lengths of the string or three diameters of the circle.

Test this experiment. Four or five members of the class should independently lay out, as carefully as possible, circles of string of a definite length, say 4 feet. Now measure the diameters, divide the 4-foot circumferences by your measured diameters, and carry out the division to six places. When you report your results in class you will begin to understand the problem of trying to determine this ratio that confronted the Greeks and others until the eighteenth century when this result was finally proven to be an irrational number. Hence, the familiar formula for the circumference of the circle: $C = \pi d$, where π is the irrational number under discussion.

Numbers such as π have been a special challenge to mathematicians throughout the ages. In the year 1615, a German mathematician Ludolf van Ceulen computed the value of π to 35 decimal places in an attempt to discover a repeating series and so show it to be a rational number. In the nineteenth century an English mathematician William Shanks spent years of his life computing the value of π to 707 places. With the advent of the computer, π has now been calculated to over 100,000 places.

It is probably worth noting that the term *irrational* as used in this text is not a psychological term but simply a word chosen some time ago to refer to those real numbers which are not rational. Because of its psychological connotation, the word *irrational* is an unfortunate adjective to attach to these very real and valuable numbers. For example $\sqrt{2}$, $\sqrt{7}$, $\sqrt{3}$, and π are all useful numbers and are just as real as any rational number and, as we have seen, are absolutely necessary to solve some equations, such as $c^2 = 1^2 + 1^2$.

The irrational numbers complete the number line in that we can place the elements of the union of the two disjoint sets Ra and Irr in a one-to-one correspondence with the set of points on the number line.

We stated earlier that we will show there are a large number of irrationals, and we implied the anomaly of there being "more" elements in the set of Irr than in Ra. Let us pursue this matter further. Is $3 + \sqrt{2}$ an irrational number? Let us prove that $3 + \sqrt{2} \in Irr$ by contradiction.

Assume $3 + \sqrt{2} = N$, where N is a rational number. Then $\sqrt{2} = N - 3$, which, because of closure, must also be a rational number. But this is a contradiction, because we have shown that $\sqrt{2}$ is irrational. Hence, $3 + \sqrt{2}$ is an irrational number.

Similarly $3 - \sqrt{2}$, $3 \cdot \sqrt{2}$, and $\sqrt{2} \div 3$ are irrational numbers. Thus, we see that given a rational number (3 in this case), we can use it to obtain *at least* four irrational numbers.[2] That is, given any rational number N, we can immediately write down four unique irra-

---

[2] This implies the four numbers are different. Can you be sure $3 + \sqrt{2}$ differs from $3 \cdot \sqrt{2}$? To show that $a + \sqrt{b} \neq a \cdot \sqrt{b}$ ($a, b \in R$ and $\sqrt{b} \in Irr$) is an interesting and not too difficult exercise. Prove it by contradiction.

tional numbers associated with N by using any one irrational number in conjunction with N and our four standard operations. For example, $N + \pi$, $N - \pi$, $N \cdot \pi$, and $N \div \pi$. Thus, we see that Irr is an infinite set, just by changing the value of N in $N + \pi$. Furthermore, we could combine N with another irrational to obtain four more unique members of the set of Irr and then with another, and another, *ad infinitum.* Intuitively then, might we not conclude that there are more elements in the set Irr than in the set Ra?

We could raise the same question about the sets Ra and C, and answer it with the same logic. Between any two elements of C, are there not an infinite number of elements of Ra? Consequently, are there not more elements in Ra than in C? But C has an infinite number of elements, as do the sets Ra and Irr; so how can one be larger than the other? This is an intuitive paradox! Is there a difference in size among infinities? It is left to the serious student to investigate this interesting paradox. To pose this same type of question simply, we ask "is the set of even counting numbers a proper subset of the counting numbers?" That is, are there fewer even counting numbers, then, than counting numbers? Yet, we must also remember to ask, is each set an infinite set? The answers to these three questions are respectively: yes; no; yes.

To provoke your thoughts even further, we note that $N(Ra)$ *does equal* $N(C) = N(I)$. *But* $N(Irr) > N(Ra)$. Proofs for these statements are beyond the scope of this text, but these statements are true and are given to illustrate the value of intuition in forming hypotheses only. *Intuition can be a most unreliable and invalid basis for forming conclusions.* Intuition tends to break down when we deal with something outside our field of experience. How many or us have experienced an infinite set?

EXERCISES
1.7

1. Is the set Irr closed with respect to the operation multiplication? Explain your answer.

2. Consider the sets C, I, Ra, Irr, and R. Which of these are closed under the operation division?

3. Which of the sets in problem 2 are subsets of the other sets mentioned?

4.   Which pairs of sets in problem 2 are disjoint sets?

5.   Prove that $a - \sqrt{b} \neq \sqrt{b}/a$, where $a \in Ra$, $\sqrt{b} \in Irr$, and $a \neq 0$.

1.8   The RST Properties

Before summarizing our review of the real number system we should review at least a few of the relationships with which we continually work. Do you recall the *RST* properties? A relation that has *reflexive, symmetric,* and *transitive* properties is said to be an *equivalence relation.* Such a relation partitions the reference set into disjoint subsets called equivalence classes in such a way that each element of the reference set becomes a member of one and only one subset.

Reflexive Property

A relation is reflexive if and only if each element of the set has the specified relationship to itself. For example, consider the relation "in the same row as" and the set of students in your classroom. (This assumes you are seated in rows.) Are you "in the same row as" yourself? Is each other student in the same row as himself? Since the answer must be yes, this relation has the reflexive property. If every element of the set on which a relation (call it Z) is defined is related to itself, then Z has the reflexive property. We write aZa, where a is an element of the set.

Symmetric Property

A relation is symmetric if for every possible case that a has the given relation to b (a, b are elements of the same set) b will have the same relation to a. Consider again the relation "is in the same row as." If you are in the same row as Joe, must Joe be in the same row as you? We see that for any one student who is in the same row as a second student, it must follow that the second student is in the same row as the first. If aZb for all a, b in the set, then bZa.

Transitive Property

A relation is transitive if when one element of a set is so related to a second element of the set, and the second is so related to a third, then the first is also so related to the third. If aZb and bZc for all a, b, and c in the set, then aZc. Continuing with our same example, if you are in the same row as Joe, and Joe is in the same row as Sue, then you are in the same row as Sue.

Since the relation "is in the same row as" satisfies all three properties defined above over the set of students in your class, it is an equivalence relation. Each of you is in one and only one row. This equivalence relation has divided the class into disjoint sets whose union is the entire set.

Perhaps we can appreciate these ideas more readily if we consider a relation that is not an equivalence relation. Let us test the relation "is greater than" to see if it meets the criteria of an equivalence relation on the set of real numbers.

1. No element can be greater than itself, that is, since $a = a$, it must follow that $a > a$ is false.
   Therefore, $>$ is *not* reflexive.

2. If $5 > 3$, then 3 cannot be greater than 5.
   Therefore, $>$ is *not* symmetric.

3. If $a > b$ and $b > c$, we know from the definition of "is greater than" that $a = b + k$ (k positive) and $b = c + m$ (m positive), and therefore $a = c + m + k$. But since $a = c + (m + k)$ and $(m + k)$ is positive, we know again, by definition, that $a > c$.
   Therefore, $>$ *is* transitive.

Since the relation $>$ does not satisfy all three of the *RST* properties, $>$ is not an equivalence relation. The relation "is equal to" is an equivalence relation. In brief, $a = a$; therefore the relation is reflexive. If $a = b$, then $b = a$, and the relation is symmetric. If $a = b$ and $b = c$, then $a = c$, and the relation is transitive. You should consider the relation $\geq$ or "is greater than or equal to."

To connect these ideas to something with which we are familiar, consider the disjoint subsets into which the set of fractions is partitioned by the relation "is equivalent to." (First, you should verify that this is an equivalence relation.) Is not every fraction a member of one and only one subset? For example, the fraction $\frac{24}{36}$ is a member of the subset we ordinarily call $\frac{2}{3}$, and all fractions that are equivalent to $\frac{2}{3}$ are members of this class. We call the fraction $\frac{2}{3}$ the *reduced representative* of the class.

EXERCISES
1.8

1. Discuss the *RST* properties of:

    a. "is less than" (on the set *R*)
    b. "divides exactly" (on the set *C*)
    c. "is 3 miles from" (on the set of all points in a plane)
    d. "is an even number when multiplied by" (on the set *C*)
    e. "is the square root of" (on the set *W*, the set of counting numbers and zero)
    f. "is the same age as" (on the set of all U.S. citizens)

2. Which of the relations in problem 1 is an equivalence relation? Into what subsets or equivalence classes does the relation partition the original (or reference) set? Is any element in more than one subset? Is any element not in a subset?

1.9   The Real Number System

Let us summarize our review of the real number system diagrammatically in Figure 1-1. We know that the set of counting numbers *C* is a subset of the set of integers *I*, since the set *C* was expanded to the set *I* to achieve closure under subtraction. Again, to gain closure under division (except by zero), the set *I* was expanded to the set of rational numbers *Ra*. Finally, to complete the number line, the set *Irr* was unioned with the set *Ra* to form the set of real numbers *R*.

We say that the real number system is a *complete ordered field*; the real number system being the union of *Irr* and *Ra* together with the operations of (+) and (·), which satisfy a number of properties such as closure, commutativity, and associativity. A rigorous definition of a field is delayed until a later chapter when the underlying ideas will be more meaningful and interesting to you.

The important point at this juncture is to remember that the real number system is *complete*. In the development of the real number system from *C* to *W* to *I* to *Ra* and to *Ra* ∪ *Irr*, we identified at each stage new points on the number line. With the union of *Irr* and *Ra*, the line has been completed and each point has been identified.

In completing our review, we should remember:

    1. The two operations (+) and (·) used in the real number system

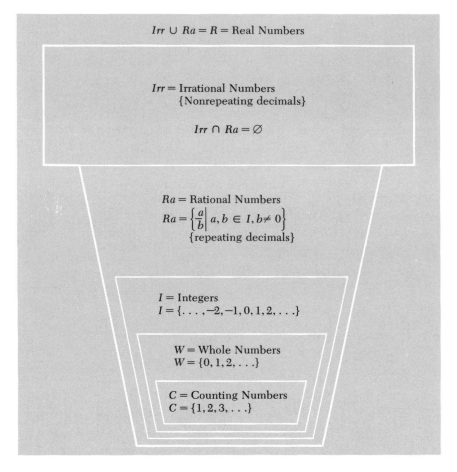

$Irr \cup Ra = R =$ Real Numbers

$Irr =$ Irrational Numbers
{Nonrepeating decimals}

$Irr \cap Ra = \varnothing$

$Ra =$ Rational Numbers
$$Ra = \left\{ \frac{a}{b} \,\middle|\, a, b \in I, b \neq 0 \right\}$$
{repeating decimals}

$I =$ Integers
$I = \{\ldots, -2, -1, 0, 1, 2, \ldots\}$

$W =$ Whole Numbers
$W = \{0, 1, 2, \ldots\}$

$C =$ Counting Numbers
$C = \{1, 2, 3, \ldots\}$

Figure 1-1

are binary operations, and the set of real numbers is closed under each of these operations.

2. The commutative property holds for both operations

$$a + b = b + a \qquad \text{and} \qquad a \cdot b = b \cdot a$$

3. The associative property holds for both operations

$$(a + b) + c = a + (b + c) \qquad \text{and} \qquad (a \cdot b) \cdot c = a \cdot (b \cdot c)$$

4. Multiplication is distributive over addition

$$a \cdot (b + c) = a \cdot b + a \cdot c$$

5. An element (0) exists such that

$$a + 0 = a$$

for any element a. 0 is called the *additive identity*. Also, an element (1) exists such that

$$a \cdot 1 = a$$

for any element a. 1 is called the *multiplicative identity*.

6. For each element $a \in R$, there exists another element $-a \in R$, called the *additive inverse*, such that the sum of the two elements is the additive identity

$$a + (-a) = 0$$

7. For each element $a \in R$, except 0, there exists another element $1/a \in R$, called its *reciprocal* (multiplicative inverse), such that the product of the two elements is the multiplicative identity 1. Thus,

$$\frac{a}{b} \cdot \frac{b}{a} = 1$$

Division by zero is undefined and not permitted.

8. The set is dense, since for any two different numbers corresponding to points on the number line, there exists a third number corresponding to a point lying between the first two.

9. The set is ordered, since for any two elements a, b exactly one of three statements is true: either $a < b$, $b < a$, or $a = b$. This is the *trichotomy property*.

10. The element 0 has the property that $0 \cdot a = 0$ for all a in the set. Furthermore, if $a \cdot b = 0$, then either a or b must be 0; and if $a + b = 0$, then a is the additive inverse of b.

11. The operation of division is defined in terms of multiplication as $a \div b = q$ if and only if $a = bq$, $b \neq 0$.

12. The operation of subtraction is defined in terms of addition. That is, $a - b = c$ if and only if $a = b + c$.

13. The cancellation law holds. If $ab = ac$ and $a \neq 0$, then $b = c$; if $a + b = a + c$, then $b = c$.

14. For $a < b$ there exists a positive element c such that $a + c = b$. And conversely, if $c > 0$ and $a + c = b$, we know that $a < b$.

15. An equivalence relation Z is one that partitions the set on which it is defined into disjoint sets. An equivalence relation

satisfies the *RST* properties:

Reflexive: *aZa* for all *a*;
Symmetric: if *aZb*, then *bZa* for all *a* and *b*;
Transitive: if *aZb* and *bZc*, then *aZc* for all *a*, *b*, and *c*.

CHAPTER REVIEW TEST ⎯⎯⎯⎯⎯⎯⎯⎯⎯⎯⎯⎯⎯⎯⎯

Before proceeding to algebra and other new material in the follow-ing chapters, you should be able to do all of the following exercises. They are designed to measure your knowledge of the basic symbols, language, facts, and ideas learned in the development of the real number system and to test your computational ability with these tools.

1. If $A = \{0, 1, 2\}$, $B = \{-2, -1, 0, 1\}$, $C = \{2, 3\}$, and $D = \{x | -1 \leq x < 5\}$, find

    a. $A \cap B$ e. $B \cap D$
    b. $A \cup C$ f. $(A \cup B) \cup D$
    c. $B \cap C$ g. $A \cup (B \cup D)$
    d. $A \cap D$ h. $(A \cap B) \cap C$

2. If the universe is the set of counting numbers, write the com-plement of set *A* above in descriptive form.

3. Find $H \cap K$, if *H* and *K* are disjoint sets.

4. Indicate the property that justifies each step.

    a. $14 \cdot 19 = 14 \cdot (10 + 9)$ *ans.*   base ten system
    b. $= 14 \cdot 10 + 14 \cdot 9$ *ans.*   distributive property
    c. $= 10 \cdot 14 + 9 \cdot 14$
    d. $= 10 \cdot (10 + 4) + 9 \cdot (10 + 4)$
    e. $= (10 \cdot 10 + 10 \cdot 4) + (9 \cdot 10 + 9 \cdot 4)$
    f. $= 100 + (10 \cdot 4 + 9 \cdot 10) + 9 \cdot 4$
    g. $= 100 + (10 \cdot 4 + 10 \cdot 9) + 9 \cdot 4$
    h. $= 100 + 10 \cdot (4 + 9) + 9 \cdot 4$
    i. $= 100 + 10 \cdot (4 + 9) + 4 \cdot 9$
    j. $= 100 + 4 \cdot 9 + 10 \cdot (4 + 9)$

5. Does the associative property hold for division on set I? Illustrate your answer with a numerical example.

6. Discuss the RST properties of the following relations:

   a. "is taller than" (on the set of all college students).
   b. "is the sister of" (on the set of U.S. armed forces personnel).

7. Simplify the following expressions.

   a. $\dfrac{2 + \frac{1}{4}}{2 - \frac{1}{4}}$ b. $\dfrac{3(1 - \frac{2}{3})}{4(1 + \frac{3}{4})}$ c. $-\frac{-2}{-3} + (-6) + \frac{-4}{5}$

8. Explain and justify with properties of the real number system each step necessary to find $\frac{-2}{5} \div \frac{6}{7}$.

9. Is the set Ra closed under the operation ($\div$)? Explain your answer.

10. Define the set R in terms of Ra and Irr.

11. Write the equivalent decimal fraction for

   a. $\frac{1}{9}$ b. $\frac{11}{15}$ c. $\frac{126}{500}$

12. If a, b are elements of I, find a and b such that

   $$\frac{a}{b} = 0.9\overline{15}$$

13. How can you show that your answer to problem 12 cannot be further "reduced"?

14. Prove if $ax < bx$ and $a < b$, then $x > 0$.

15. Difficulties often arise from careless or inaccurate reading and identification of the problem; hence, the not uncommon fear of "word problems." Solve the following:

   a. Let $n \in C$ such that n is divisible by 5. What is the smallest n such that a remainder of 2 is obtained when n is divided by 9?
   b. Of 11,395 students, 620 were absent one day. To the near-

est one-tenth of one percent, what percent were present?

c. The scale on an architect's drawing is 1 foot to $\frac{1}{8}$ inch. A distance of 18 inches on the drawing represents how many yards in the structure?

d. Given a universe as the area described by a rectangle 8 inches long and 5 inches wide and a subset of the universe as the area described by a right triangle having sides 3, 4, and 5 inches such that the 5-inch side of the triangle coincides with one of the 5-inch sides of the universe, show the complement of the subset by appropriately shading a freehand drawing of the above.

e. What distance must a runner run to run a 4-minute mile?

f. In problem 4 had we used any two "teens" instead of 14 and 19 the final step would have read: $100 + a \cdot b + 10(a + b)$, with a being the unit digit of the first teen and b being the unit digit of the second teen. In words, write this last statement as a rule for multiplying two teens, and check your rule by applying it to $17 \cdot 18$.

CHECKING YOUR WORK

page
6

1. a. $A \cap B = \{-2, 0\}$. This answer is read "the intersection of sets A and B is the set whose elements are -2 and 0." This means that -2 and 0 are the elements common to both A and B.

   b. $A \cap C = \{-2, -1, 0, 1, 2\}$.

   c. $A \cap D =$ the empty set or $\emptyset$, or $\{\quad\}$.

   d. $C \cup D = I$. This answer is read "the union of sets C and D is the set of all integers." This new set contains every element found in C or D.

2. Disjoint pairs include AD, BD, and CD. Disjoint sets are two sets with no elements in common.

3. The complement of C is $\{x | x > 2\}$, $\{x | x \geq 3\}$, or in *tabular* form $\{3, 4, 5, \ldots\}$. The complement of a set is the set of all elements of the universe that are not in the original set. Thus, the union of C and its complement is U.

Return to page 6

<table>
<tr><td rowspan="5">**page 10**</td><td>Associative property of addition:</td><td>$(2 + 3) + 4 = 2 + (3 + 4)$</td></tr>
<tr><td>Associative property of multiplication:</td><td>$(2 \cdot 3) \cdot 4 = 2 \cdot (3 \cdot 4)$</td></tr>
<tr><td>Commutative property of addition:</td><td>$2 + 3 = 3 + 2$</td></tr>
<tr><td>Commutative property of multiplication:</td><td>$2 \cdot 3 = 3 \cdot 2$</td></tr>
</table>

DEFINITION   The *associative* property of addition provides that in the set of counting numbers C the sum of several elements is the same regardless of how they are grouped. That is, if $a, b, c \in C$, then

$$(a + b) + c = a + (b + c)$$

DEFINITION   The commutative property of multiplication provides that in the set of counting numbers C the product of several elements is the same regardless of how they are ordered. That is, if $a, b, c \in C$, then

$$a \cdot b = b \cdot a$$

and

$$a \cdot b \cdot c = c \cdot a \cdot b = c \cdot b \cdot a$$

Return to page 10

page 13

1. The set of even counting numbers is closed under multiplication.

    PROOF   Given $a \cdot b = c$, where $a, b, c \in C$.

    a. If a and b are both even, they each have a factor of 2 and can be written as $2g$ and $2h$, where g and $h \in C$.
    b. From the given statement, then, we have $a \cdot b = c$ or $2g \cdot 2h = c$.
    c. Using the commutative property of multiplication, we can therefore write $2 \cdot 2 \cdot g \cdot h = c$ or $4gh = c$. For this to be true however c must also have a factor of 4 (since C is closed under multiplication), which means c itself is an even counting number.

2. The set of odd counting numbers is not closed under addition.

This can be proved by contradiction. For example, $3+5=8$ and 8 is not in the set of odd counting numbers.

3. Choose the set of prime numbers, which is not closed under addition. For example, $7+11=18$ and 18 is not prime.

Return to page 13

page 16

1. $\frac{1}{7} = 0.\overline{142857}$ 3. $\frac{11}{12} = 0.91\overline{6}$

2. $\frac{5}{9} = 0.\overline{5}$ 4. $\frac{27}{40} = 0.6750\overline{0}$

5. All rational numbers are members of the set of repeating decimals, because from the division algorithm we have $a = bq + r$, where $a, b, q, r \in C, b \neq 0$ and $0 \leq r < b$ such that in the process of dividing:

$$b \overline{\smash{)}\, a.000} \begin{array}{l} .dhl \\ \underline{c\ e} \\ \quad f0 \\ \quad \underline{i\ j} \\ \qquad k\ 0 \\ \qquad \underline{mn} \\ \qquad a \end{array}$$

The remainder obtained after each partial division must be less than the divisor b. Hence, the maximum number of possible *different* remainders that can be obtained is finite and is equal to $b-1$, assuming $r \neq 0$. Therefore, before we find b number of partial quotients, the remainder must repeat one of the previous remainders, and at this point the problem becomes the same division problem encountered earlier.

To illustrate, in finding the decimal equivalent for $\frac{1}{7}$ in problem 1, you note the remainders you obtained were 3, 2, 6, 4, 5, and 1. But 1 divided by 7 is the original problem; so if you continue, you will find the same series of integers repeating in the quotient. In this case all $b-1$, or 6, possible different remainders were obtained before the repetition began. Thus, since the remainder must be less than 7, the repetition *must* begin at least by the seventh partial quotient.

But what if the remainder is zero? Then it is a terminating decimal, and if you continued the algorithm you would have the integer zero repeating itself, just as you found in problem 4.

Return to page 17

page 19

1. First, factor the shorter numeral 4950.

$$
\begin{array}{r}
11 \\
5\,\overline{)\,55} \\
5\,\overline{)\,275} \\
3\,\overline{)\,825} \\
3\,\overline{)\,2475} \\
2\,\overline{)\,4950}
\end{array}
$$

2. Seeing that $4950 = 2 \cdot 3 \cdot 3 \cdot 5 \cdot 5 \cdot 11$, you need only check to see if the numeral 11,069 contains any of the factors 2, 3, 5, or 11.

3. Since none of these divides 11,069 exactly, the two numerals have no common factors, and they are therefore the simplest representative of 11,069/4950.

Return to page 19

2

LINEAR EQUATIONS

Now that we have completed a review of the development of the real number system we can embark with confidence upon the study of algebra—or so it is tempting to state. The error or misleading implication of this statement is not in the use of the word "confidence," but in the division it implies between the study of the real number system and algebra. One does not conclude a study of the number system and then embark on a study of algebra; the two sets of knowledge are not disjoint! You should realize that algebra is a logical extension of the real number system.

This erroneous idea that arithmetic and algebra are two disjoint sets was instilled in some of us when we "finished" arithmetic in the eighth grade and then took up a new subject—algebra—in the ninth grade. Many of us, for example, learned "$a(b+c)=ab+ac$" as a new fact, rather than as a generalization of what we had been doing for years in arithmetic—a generalization most pupils in elementary schools today know as the distributive property. We also learned that $ab + ac = a(b + c)$ was true because of a new approach called "factoring" rather than looking at this statement as a result of a generalization of facts we already knew or as a result of the symmetric property of the relation "equals."

If there is one goal towards which every word of this text is aimed, it is to show that there are interrelationships between the mathematics contained in this text and the mathematics previously known to you.

2.1 The Meaning of Algebra

When we expanded our number system from the set C to set I, we did so because of the need for closure under subtraction. Similarly, when we expanded to the set Ra and then formed the union of Ra and *Irr* to complete the number line, we accomplished these expansions from logical needs. In each case we obtained a closure that opened an entirely new area of workability for numbers; one in which mathematics could be applied to previously unsolved problems; a new area in which our tools of mathematics could be used to measure, build, explain, and prove. We can establish a need for further extension of the number system, but first, we must consider the basic concept of algebra itself.

We make the following definition:

DEFINITION 2-1 ————————————————————————————

Algebra, taken from the Arabic *al-jabr*, literally means the reunion of broken parts and is that branch of mathematics which deals in the most *general* way with the operations, properties, and relations of *numbers*.

———————————————————————————————————————

Much of algebra is devoted to the solution of practical problems arising from everyday life. Solutions are found through the general use of the relations, properties, and operations of the real number system, which we have just reviewed. A large portion of the basic ideas and facts of algebra are learned today in elementary schools.

Many illustrations of the utilitarian aspect of algebra can be made. For example, when a fifth grade student solves a "word problem" he often uses algebra in the sense that he represents the unknown number by the literal numeral N or x. For example, "given 48 cookies, how many can you guarantee each of 14 children at a party?" In solving this problem, our fifth grader might think "fourteen children each eating N cookies must eat a total number of cookies which is less than or equal to 48, or $14 \cdot N \le 48$." Dividing both sides by 14, he finds $N \le 48 \div 14$; therefore, the answer is $3\frac{6}{14}$. This process of thinking and doing can be termed algebra.

At a more sophisticated level, the algebraic process, or algebraic thinking, becomes even more useful. Consider this problem: "You are to drive to a neighboring city 60 miles away along the turnpike at a constant rate of 70 miles per hour, but on the return trip you must drive more slowly. If you can allow only 2 hours for travel, what is the slowest constant speed you can drive on the return trip?"

Intuitively we might think as follows: "Well, since the distance is 60 miles, if I drive at 60 miles per hour both ways it should take exactly 2 hours. Therefore, I must average 60 miles per hour. Because I will drive 70 miles per hour to the city, I must drive 50 miles per hour returning, since the average of 70 and 50 is 60." Correct? No, the reasoning is incorrect. If you challenge this, then by all means study the discussion and accompanying explanation when you

CHECK YOUR WORK on page 61

Other applications of algebra are evident in solving such problems as:

1. Will more interest be earned by investing $100,000 per year at a simple interest rate of 5% per annum than by investing the same amount at $4\frac{1}{2}\%$ per annum compounded quarterly? Your answer should be a definite yes! Compute and see!

2. A farmer herded ten cows into a pasture of grass 4 inches high. He herded the cows out 12 days later after they had eaten the grass down to 1 inch in height. When the grass was again 4 inches high, the farmer herded in twenty cows. These twenty cows ate the grass down to 1 inch in five days. How fast did the farmer's grass grow? (Assume constant weather conditions and a constant eating rate by the cows.)

Does this question sound as if it cannot be answered from the data given? Not so! The key to the *logic* of answering the question is that the grass grows *during the time* the cows eat as well as when the pasture is not being grazed. The key to obtaining the numerical *answer* is algebraic skill. (For those of you who are taking this course because you enjoy learning and doing puzzles the answer is $\frac{1}{10}$ of an inch per day. Do you agree?)

3. An oil refinery can produce gasoline at a profit of 20¢ per barrel and jet fuel at a profit of 10¢ per barrel. A maximum of 10,000 barrels of both can be produced by the company each day, of which 2000 must be jet fuel to satisfy an airline contract and

1000 must be gasoline to satisfy a local distributor contract. Both the airline and the distributor want to increase their contracts with the oil company. The oil company wants to arrange the increases so that a maximum profit is realized by the company. The jet fuel must be delivered a distance of 10 miles and the gasoline a distance of 30 miles. The oil company has only enough trucks to transport 210,000 barrel-miles each day. (Barrel-miles are computed by multiplying the number of full barrels by the number of miles transported.) How many barrels per day should the oil company increase its contract with each party?[1]

This problem is not really as difficult to solve as it might first appear. First, the problem must be put into algebraic terms, and then its solution can be found readily when that branch of mathematics known as linear programming is used. We will solve this problem later in the text, but first we must relate the idea of lines and curves to that of equations. Much of this chapter is devoted to the interrelationship between "algebraic" and "geometric" concepts.

2.2 The Cartesian Plane

Many students find it difficult to appreciate the linear nature of a simple equation, such as

$$x + 2y = 5$$

Indeed, until the seventeenth century no one truly appreciated the "straight line" property of such simple equations. This type of understanding is what we seek in this chapter.

René Descartes, the great French philosopher, mathematician, and physicist of the first half of the seventeenth century, invented a system of graphically portraying relations between numbers. The system of rectangular coordinates is called "Cartesian coordinates" in honor of its inventor Descartes. Although Descartes may not have realized the full impact that his discovery would have, its result has been the valuable technique of dealing with geometry in terms of algebra known as *analytic geometry*. In short, the wedding of

---

[1] Adapted from George A. W. Boehm and the Editors of *Fortune, The New World of Math* (New York City: The Dial Press, 1959), page 110.

algebra and geometry by Descartes resulted in the birth of analytic geometry.

The Cartesian coordinates are commonly studied in secondary schools. You should recall that the horizontal axis is labeled the x axis and the vertical axis the y axis. Through the use of such a system, simple equations are seen to have a linear property, i.e., a straight-line quality. Linear equations were often called simple equations in older texts,[2] not because they are simple to deal with, but because the unknowns or variables in simple equations are always of the first degree — none of the variables is squared or raised to any power except 1. A more precise definition is

DEFINITION 2-2 ——————————————————————————————

A **linear equation** is one that can be reduced to the form $ax + by = c$, where x and y are variables and a, b, c are real numbers, with either a or b or both not zero.

To profit from Descartes' work, let us plot on the Cartesian coordinate system several elements of the solution set of the linear equation $x + 2y = 5$. If in the equation x equals 5, then y must equal 0 for the equality to hold. The ordered solution pair $(5, 0)$ can now be plotted when we recall several other facts illustrated in Figure 2-1 about Cartesian coordinates.

The x axis represents the real number line with negative values corresponding to points on the line to the left of the point named zero and positive values to the right of zero. The y axis represents the real number line with negative values corresponding to points below zero and positive values to those above zero. The intersection of the two axes is at their zero points and is called the *origin* of the coordinate system. The two axes together are called *coordinate axes*. The x axis is known as the *axis of abscissas* and the y axis as the *axis of ordinates*. Ordinarily, the same set of convenient units is scaled off on both axes, but it is not necessary that the scales always be the same.

——————————————————

[2] If you have never paged through an algebra text published around the turn of the century, you should try to find one in the library and do so. They are usually quite concise. For example, see: G. A. Wentworth, *New School Algebra* (Boston: Ginn and Company, 1898), pp. 15, 16.

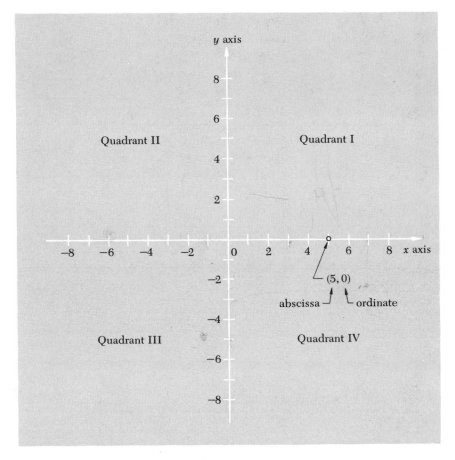

**Figure
2-1**

Since both axes represent the real number line, we can view their plane as the set of all points corresponding to the cross product of the real numbers with themselves. Symbolically, if sets X and Y both equal the set of real numbers, then

$$X \times Y = \{(x, y) | x \in X \text{ and } y \in Y\}$$

The Cartesian, or rectangular, coordinate system associates the set of ordered pairs (x, y) with the set of all points in the plane. If we are interested in the point identified by the ordered pair $(5, 0)$, we speak of the point P whose coordinates are 5 and 0. The x value 5 is called the *abscissa* of P, and the y value 0 is called the *ordinate* of P. Clearly this point is different from the point associated with the ordered pair $(0, 5)$ because the points do not have the same abscissas and ordinates.

You should note the relationship between Cartesian coordinates and the system long used in geography to identify any point on the map of the world. Given a pair of numerals representing North latitude and East longitude, only one point on the map is identified. Why can we *not* state that each point on a *globe* is associated with only one ordered pair of numerals representing North latitude and East longitude? (Hint: Consider the North Pole.)

We often use a coordinate system in a less sophisticated form in giving directions in our own cities. When we say "go over four blocks and up three," we are designating one and only one location with respect to our location. An advantage of the Cartesian system is that when two numbers are used to identify a location on the plane, they are an *ordered* pair of numbers, and we need not designate "up," "down," or "latitude-north," "longitude-east." The point $P(a, b)$, for example, is located in the Cartesian plane simply by noting the intersection of the perpendicular line drawn through point a on the x axis with the perpendicular line drawn through point b on the y axis.

The two axes divide the plane into four parts called *quadrants* (see Figure 2-1). Given that a and b are each real numbers greater than 0, plot a sufficient number of points to make it clear that

$P(a, b)$ is in Quadrant I
$P(-a, b)$ is in Quadrant II
$P(-a, -b)$ is in Quadrant III
$P(a, -b)$ is in Quadrant IV

EXERCISES
2.2

1. Plot the following points:

    a. $P(2, 4)$ e. $P(-6, 0)$ i. $P(-4, -4)$
    b. $P(4, 0)$ f. $P(-1, -5)$ j. $P(-1, 6)$
    c. $P(0, 6)$ g. $P(7, -3)$ k. $P(3, -1)$
    d. $P(-3, 2)$ h. $P(0, -6)$ l. $P(-6, -1)$

2. Determine by inspection the quadrant in which each of the following points is located:

    a. $P(3, 3)$ e. $P(-1, -5)$
    b. $P(-3, -3)$ f. $P(-4, 6)$
    c. $P(-3, 3)$ g. $P(48, 92)$
    d. $P(3, -3)$ h. $P(73, -37)$

2.3 Plotting Collinear Points

In Figure 2-1 we plotted the point identified by the ordered pair $(5, 0)$. This ordered pair corresponded to a solution to the equation $x + 2y = 5$. Let us find two more solutions for this equation and then plot all three solutions on the same graph.

Suppose $x = -5$ in the equation $x + 2y = 5$. We write

$-5 + 2y = 5$	(replacing x with -5)
$2y = 10$	(adding 5 to each member)
$y = 5$	(dividing each member by 2)

Thus a second solution to the equation is $x = -5$ and $y = 5$. Similarly, if $x = 1$, $y = 2$ to satisfy the equation. These last two solutions correspond to the ordered pairs $(-5, 5)$ and $(1, 2)$, respectively. From now on (to facilitate our work), we identify a point on a graph with the ordered pair (a, b) and speak of "the point (a, b)."

The point $(-5, 5)$ is located on the graph in Figure 2-2 by identify-

Figure 2-2

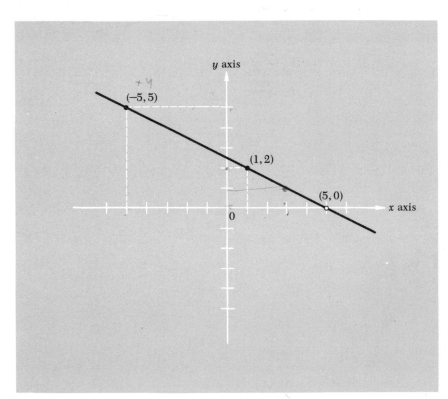

ing the intersection of the perpendicular to the x axis passing through the point $x = -5$ and the perpendicular to the y axis passing through the point $y = 5$. The point $(1, 2)$ is located in a similar manner.

The student can see from Figure 2-2 that the three points appear to be *collinear*, i.e., they all seem to lie on the same straight line, as indeed they do. Hence, the name *linear equation* – an equation whose graph is a straight line. Conversely, the coordinates of every point on a straight line satisfy the linear equation represented by the line. Hence, we have the following definition:

DEFINITION 2-3 ————————————————————————————

A **straight line** is the set of all points whose coordinates satisfy a linear equation.

——

**EXERCISES
2.3**

Plot enough points to sketch the line identified by each of the following linear equations.

1. $x - y = 0$ 5. $x - 2y = 4$
2. $x + y = 2$ 6. $2x + 3y = -3$
3. $x = y$ 7. $2x = y + 1$
4. $2y = x + 4$ 8. $y = -\frac{3}{4}x - \frac{1}{2}$

9. How many ordered pairs are necessary to graph each line?

10. Why would you plot at least three points in graphing a line?

11. What point would you select as the *origin* on your world map?

12. With which term would you associate latitude – abscissa or ordinate?

13. How could you map the location of chairs, desks, and other equipment in your classroom?

2.4   Identifying Linear Equations

We have considered some simple equations in two variables and the lines they describe. How about an equation with only one variable to the first power such as $x = 5$? This too can be graphed. Try it and then

CHECK YOUR WORK on page 62

Do not confuse an equation such as $x = 3/y$ with linear equations. Here we find that if we multiply both sides of the equation by y, we have $xy = 3$, which is not a linear equation as previously defined.

EXERCISES
2.4

Identify by inspection those equations which are not linear.

1. $x = -4$

2. $y = 3$

3. $y = 0$

4. $3x + 7 = 2 - y$

5. $\dfrac{x}{3} - \dfrac{y}{2} = y$

6. $2x - \dfrac{2}{y} = 4$

7. $\dfrac{\frac{1}{2} - \frac{1}{4}}{x} = 4$

8. $-9 = 3xy$

9. Without graphing or even plotting a point, describe the graphs of each of the equations of problems 1, 2, and 3 above. Then, plot a sufficient number of points in each case to verify your answer.

2.5   Intercepts and Slope

Every linear equation can be reduced to the general form $ax + by = c$, as stated in Definition 2-2. For example, in Exercises 2.4, the equation of problem 1 can be written $1x + 0y = -4$, where $a = 1$, $b = 0$, and $c = -4$ in the general equation. Similarly, the equation of problem 4 can be written $3x + y = 2 - 7$ or $3x + 1y = -5$, which is might also be related to the slope. In Figure 2-3, note the change in values of y and x necessary to move from (1, 2) to (5, 0). Beginning at point (1, 2), we move "down" two steps and then "over" four steps to the right—down two, over four. If we begin at point (−5, 5), how do we move to get to point (1, 2)? We move down three and over six.

Suppose from point (1, 2) we move just half the distance we did to get to point (5, 0). That is, suppose we had moved only one step down and two steps to the right. We would again be at a point on the line, namely the point (3, 1). As long as our move is in the ratio of "one down" for every "two to the right," we always end up on the line of the equation. This ratio of "one down, two to the right" can be expressed as the fraction $-\frac{1}{2}$ or negative one divided by positive two. Notice that this is the same fraction that appears as the coefficient of x in the equation of the line when written in the form of $y = -\frac{1}{2}x + \frac{5}{2}$.

Let us summarize. We know that the slope of a line graphed on a two-dimensional coordinate system is represented by the ratio of the number of units "up" (or "down") to the number of units "over," always to the *right*. Furthermore, if the ratio is viewed as a numeral representing "vertical over horizontal distance," we can postulate that this numeral always appears as the coefficient of x when the equation for the line is solved for y. Finally, it can be shown that the line runs downwards (from left to right) when the coefficient of x is negative, and upwards when the coefficient is positive.

We can now define slope more precisely.

DEFINITION 2-4 ───────────────────────────────────

The **slope** of a line representing a linear equation written in the form $y = mx + k$ is m.

───

In the case of the line shown in Figure 2-3 we know that its equation is $y = -\frac{1}{2}x + \frac{5}{2}$, and the slope of the line is given by $-\frac{1}{2}$, the coefficient of x. Therefore, we say the line has a slope of $-\frac{1}{2}$. The $-\frac{1}{2}$ indicates that we *descend* from any given point on the line one step and then run to the right two steps in order to determine another point on the line. (If our equation were $y = +\frac{1}{2}x + \frac{5}{2}$, the $+\frac{1}{2}$ would indicate a *rise* of one step and a run of two steps to the right.)

EXERCISES
2.5

Find the slope of the line representing each of the following equations. Plot enough points to verify your findings.

1. $x - y = 7$ 5. $y = 3x - 2$
2. $y - x = 7$ 6. $y = 5$
3. $7 - x = y$ 7. $2x = 4y - 1$
4. $2x - 3y = 0$ 8. $5x - 2 = 3 - 6y$

9. Find the y intercept of each of the lines.

10. Find the x intercept of each of the lines.

2.6   Graphs and Linear Equations

As an aid to memory, you may think of the coefficient of x as being determined by "rise over run." Of course, if the "rise" is downwards, the coefficient is negative. Conversely, if the coefficient is negative, the line runs downhill from left to right. This ratio of "rise over run," that is, the coefficient of x, is represented by the symbol m in most standard texts. The "slope" form of the general linear equation $ax + by = c$ then becomes $y = mx + k$, where $m = \dfrac{-a}{b}$ and $k = \dfrac{c}{b}$. (You should realize that changing the letters used for constants in such an equation does not change the basic concept.)

To review, let us examine the following equations:

$$2x - 3y = -6 \tag{1}$$

$$3x + y = -3 \tag{2}$$

Solving equation (1) for y, we find[3] $y = \frac{2}{3}x + 2$. Now by inspection, the slope of this line is positive. For every two units of rise from the origin, parallel to the y axis, we must travel three units to the right, parallel to the x axis. Is this sufficient information to permit us to draw the line for this equation? No, it simply gives us the slope of the line.

To obtain additional information, we determine the y intercept.

---

[3] If you are not proficient in solving such equations for y, you should go to the library, check out any standard high school beginning algebra text, and work enough exercises solving linear equations until you regain your proficiency.

Recall that the y intercept is the point at which the line intersects the y axis and is of necessity, then, that point on the line for which the abscissa is zero. If x equals zero in equation (1), $y = \frac{2}{3}x + 2$, it must follow that $y = 2$ and the point $(0, 2)$ is on the line. Do we now have sufficient information to draw the graph of the equation?

We know two things. The y intercept is the point $(0, 2)$ and the slope of the line is $\frac{2}{3}$. If, beginning at the point $(0, 2)$, we "rise" 2 units and then "run" 3 units to the right, we arrive at the point $(3, 4)$ as shown in Figure 2-4. We have now plotted two points, $(0, 2)$ and $(3, 4)$. Since two points are sufficient to determine the line, it may be drawn as in Figure 2-4. As an exercise, determine the x intercept both by "rise and run" and by solving for x when $y = 0$.

By direct substitution into the equation, verify that the coordinates of each of the three points $(0, 2)$, $(3, 4)$, and the x intercept satisfy the equation. Notice that knowledge of just one point and the slope is sufficient to draw the line.

Let us examine equation (2) in a different way. Rather than graphing a line from its equation, can we determine the equation if we are given its graph? Study Figure 2-5. Relying on what we have just learned, first notice that the graph goes downwards from left to right; consequently, the slope m is a negative real number. Second, notice that for a fall (or negative rise) of three units we run over one unit so

Figure 2-4

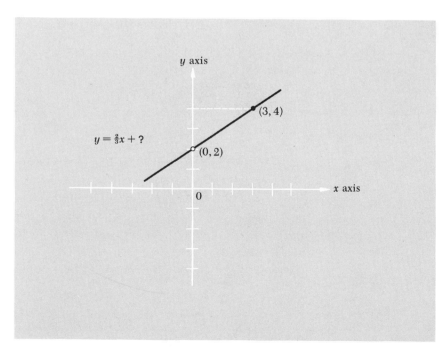

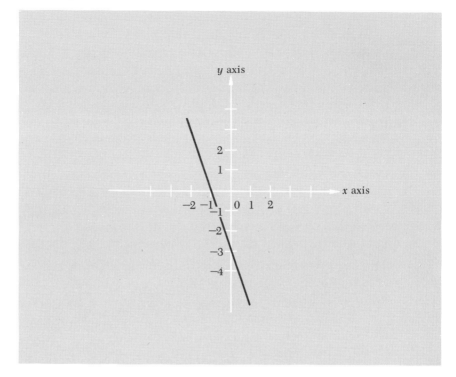

Figure 2-5

that $m = -3/1$ or simply -3. We now have sufficient information to write $y = -3x + k$. How can we determine the value of k from Figure 2-5? Answer this question as best you can and then

CHECK YOUR WORK on page 63

We have determined that:

1. A linear equation can be found from its graph.

2. The graph of a linear equation is a straight line.

3. A linear equation and its graph can be found if we are given the slope of a line and one point on that line, or if we are given any two points on the line.

EXERCISES 2.6

Find the x intercept, y intercept, and slope of each of the lines represented by the following equations.

1. $y + 3x = 0$
2. $5y - 15 = 0$
3. $x + 2y + 4 = 0$
4. $x = 4$
5. $7 + 2y = -5x$
6. $3x - 4y = 5$

7. Sketch the graph of each of the above equations.

8. Find the equation for each of the following:

    a. A line with slope $\frac{1}{2}$ through the point $(-1, 5)$

    b. A line with a slope of zero passing through the point $(3, 4)$

    c. A line through the points $(3, -12)$ and $(-8, 10)$

9. What is the slope of the line in problem 8c?

10. Sketch the graph of each of the lines in problem 8.

11. Find the equation for each of the four lines in Figure 2-6.

Figure 2-6

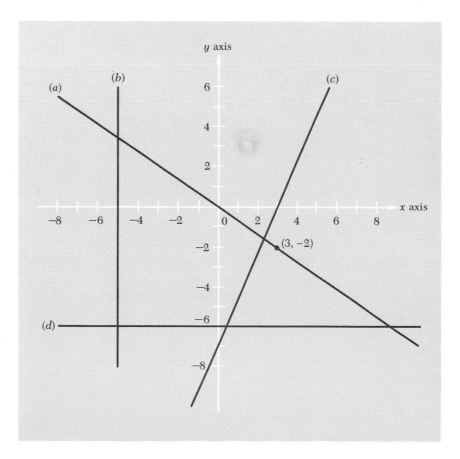

12. By inspection, how could you have found the values of k from the slope form of each equation in problem 11?

13. What generalization can you now make regarding k and the y intercept? How can this information be applied to gain more information if you are given the equation and not the graph? The graph and not the equation?

14. Write a paragraph or two discussing the slope of a linear equation when the coefficient of one variable is zero. For example, consider $x - 0y = 3$, or $0x - y = 4$.

2.7 Finding the Slope

Earlier in this chapter, we simply stated as a fact that the coordinates of any point on a line satisfy the linear equation represented by the line. This idea was developed intuitively so that it seemed acceptable to us. However, as we saw from the problem of finding the average speed when driving 70 miles per hour one way and 50 miles per hour on the return, our intuition sometimes needs rigorous checking. This is one of those times. The "fact" in question is so fundamental to mathematics that we dare not (and need not) let it stand on the basis of intuition. Proof is needed.

How can we show that any point on a given line identifies an ordered pair that satisfies the equation of the line? Let us proceed by examining the concept of slope in a more general way.

Consider problem 2.6-11 once more. When you were finding the equation for line (a) in Figure 2-6, you first found the slope by counting the number of units of rise (or fall) and placed this number over the number of units of run.

Actually, in more elegant language, you were writing the difference in y values of the two points over the difference in x values of the two points. The two known points on line (a) are $(0, 0)$ and $(3, -2)$. We can write

$$\frac{\text{the difference of } y \text{ values}}{\text{the difference of } x \text{ values}} = \frac{0 - (-2)}{0 - 3} = \frac{+2}{-3} = -\frac{2}{3} = m$$

It does not matter which point we consider first. If we had reversed the order and claimed the two known points were $(3, -2)$ and $(0, 0)$, we would have written:

$$\frac{\text{the difference of } y \text{ values}}{\text{the difference of } x \text{ values}} = \frac{-2 - 0}{3 - 0} = \frac{-2}{3} = -\frac{2}{3} = m$$

In general, for any two points (x_1, y_1) and (x_2, y_2) on the line, where $x_1 \neq x_2$ (because if $x_1 - x_2 = 0$, we would be indicating division by zero, which is not defined), we could find the slope by writing

$$\frac{\text{the difference of } y \text{ values}}{\text{the difference of } x \text{ values}} = \frac{y_1 - y_2}{x_1 - x_2} = m$$

DEFINITION 2-5 —————————————————————————————

The **equation of the slope** of the line containing the two points (x_1, y_1) and (x_2, y_2) is given by the equation

$$m = \frac{y_1 - y_2}{x_1 - x_2}$$

where $x_1 \neq x_2$. (Note: A vertical line, one of the form $x = c$, has no slope. This is the case, where $x_1 = x_2$. What would the slope be for $y = c$?)

———

EXERCISES
2.7

Find the slope of the line containing the given points.

1. (4, 2)   and (1, 1)   5. (0, 0)   and (−4, −4)
2. (−2, −4) and (1, 1)   6. (−3, 4) and (0, 4)
3. (−5, 2) and (0, 0)   7. (0, −7) and (−7, −7)
4. (0, 0)   and (4, 3)   8. (3, −2) and (3, 4)

2.8 Relationships of a Line and Its Equation

Now we are prepared to consider *any* line such as (c) in Figure 2-6. The two intercepts are seen to be the points $(0, -7)$ and $(3, 0)$. You probably solved problem 2.6-11c by first finding the slope. In this case,

$$\frac{y_1 - y_2}{x_1 - x_2} = \frac{-7 - 0}{0 - 3} = \frac{-7}{-3} = \frac{7}{3}$$

Substituting this value for m in the general equation, we obtain $y = \frac{7}{3}x + k$. There remains then only the problem of finding the value of k.

Inspection of the graph shows that when $x = 0$, $y = -7$. But from $y = \frac{7}{3}x + k$, we see that when $x = 0$, $y = k$. Therefore, $k = -7$. Checking this against the other known point, the x intercept, we note from the graph that when $y = 0$, $x = 3$; substituting these values, the equation is again reduced to $k = -7$. Hence, the equation represented by line (c) is $y = \frac{7}{3}x - 7$.

Let us now follow the same procedure to show that the coordinates of *any* point on the line must also satisfy the equation. Suppose that instead of our two known points we had been given only the points $(0, -7)$ and (a, b), where the latter is *any* point on the line representing the equation $y = \frac{7}{3}x - 7$. Now if the point (a, b) is on the line, the question we ask is "will the numbers a and b satisfy the equation?" In short, we must show that the equation holds when the values a and b are substituted for x and y. Does $b = \frac{7}{3}a - 7$ hold?

Let us proceed by finding the slope, just as we did for two known points. According to the slope equation, the slope m of the two points $(0, -7)$ and (a, b) is

$$m = \frac{-7 - b}{0 - a} = \frac{-(7 + b)}{-a} = \frac{7 + b}{a} \qquad (a \neq 0)$$

But we know the slope m of line (c) is $\frac{7}{3}$, so

$$\frac{7}{3} = \frac{7 + b}{a}$$

$7a = 3(7 + b)$	(multiplying both sides by $3a$)
$7a = 21 + 3b$	(distributing)
$7a - 21 = 3b$	(subtracting 21 from each side)
$\frac{7}{3}a - 7 = b$	(dividing both sides by 3)
$b = \frac{7}{3}a - 7$	(what we wanted to show!)

Now we have shown that for any point (a, b), $a \neq 0$, on the line (c) in Figure 2-6, the ordered pair (a, b) is an element of the solution set of the equation $y = \frac{7}{3} - 7$. Next we must ask ourselves two important questions. First, do the coordinates of any point on a line satisfy the equation of that line and, second, does any ordered pair satisfying the equation correspond to the coordinates of a point on the line?

You may be tempted to "trust" the author and accept an affirmative answer to these questions because you know it is probably true anyway and you would rather not wade through a large set of imposing symbols. But consider a moment.

We have a very good *reason* for the extension of the number system to algebra. Your work with numerals and letters using the operations and properties of the real number system will give you an insight into the interrelationships of arithmetic and algebra that you can achieve in no other way. To appreciate this fully, you will do well to pencil out for yourself each step of what follows and try to stay at least one step *ahead.* This is not an exercise which you may or may not do—this is one you *must* do.

THEOREM 2-1

If L is a nonvertical line of slope m, then a point (a, b) is on L if and only if $b = ma + k$, where m and k are real numbers.

Proof   To prove this theorem we need to show that when we are speaking of a nonvertical line and its corresponding equation

1. the coordinates of any point on the line satisfy the equation; and
2. any ordered pair satisfying the equation are coordinates of a point on the line.

Proof of point 1   The equation of a nonvertical line has the form $y = mx + k$. A nonvertical line intercepts the y axis at the point $(0, k)$; therefore this point is on the line. If we take any other point on the line such as (a, b) and use the two points in the equation of the slope, we have

$$m = \frac{b - k}{a - 0} = \frac{b - k}{a} \qquad (a \neq 0)$$

Multiplying through by a we obtain

$$ma = b - k$$
$$ma + k = b$$
$$b = ma + k$$

Thus, we see that the coordinates of any point (a, b) on a nonvertical line satisfy the equation of that line.

Proof of point 2   If an ordered pair (a, b) satisfies the equation of a line, then we know that $b = ma + k$. To prove that (a, b) are coordinates of a point on the line corresponding to the equation, we proceed by assuming the point is *not* on the line and arrive at a contradiction. Solving the given equation for m, we find

$$b = ma + k$$
$$b - k = ma$$
$$ma = b - k$$
$$m = \frac{b - k}{a} \qquad (a \neq 0)$$

We can reach a contradiction by showing this last equation to be false. We know the point $(0, k)$ lies on the line, and we have assumed (a, b) is *not* on the line. Using these two points, therefore, the slope formula cannot be satisfied. Thus,

$$m \neq \frac{b - k}{a - 0}$$

or

$$m \neq \frac{b - k}{a} \qquad (a \neq 0)$$

We have arrived at a contradiction and must conclude that our assumption is false and that (a, b) *does* lie on the line representing the equation $b = ma + k$.

Note also the fact that m and k do not depend upon the choice of a and b (or the coordinates of *any* point on a line for that matter); they depend only on the line.

Note that the theorem was stated only for nonvertical lines. The reason for this is that the slope of the vertical line is undefined. A vertical line is the graph of an equation that can be written in the form $x + 0y = c$, or $x = c$. For a point to lie on a vertical line then, the first coordinate of the point must be c and the second can be any real number z. The general description for a point on this vertical line becomes (c, z). Substitution of the ordered pair (c, z) in the equation satisfies the equation: $x + 0y = c$; $c + 0z = c$; or $c = c$. Thus, the coordinates of any point on a vertical line satisfy its equation. Can you show that any ordered pair satisfying the equation of a vertical line correspond to the coordinates of a point on the line?

SUMMARY

Algebra can be defined as the unifying thread of mathematics; or the logical extension of a number system; or the methods involved in working with the set of real numbers in accordance with the rules governing operations, properties, and relations of the real number system. We have discovered some applications of algebra to problem solving in everyday life and hinted at more sophisticated needs and uses for algebra in the worlds of business and science.

We have discovered the relationship between a linear equation and a line. If we know either the slope of a line and the coordinates of any point on it or if we know the coordinates of any two points on the line, we have sufficient information to graph the line on a system of rectangular coordinates and also to determine its equation. Given any line representing the equation $ax + by = c$ $(b \neq 0)$, its slope can be determined by inspection when the equation is solved for y. This solution is in the form of $y = mx + k$, where y and x are the values of the coordinates, m is the slope, and k is the ordinate of the y intercept. The y intercept is easily determined as the point $(0, k)$, since $x = 0$ at the y intercept. Hence, any linear equation can be graphed, and its graph is a straight line.

Finally, we have proved that the coordinates of every point on a line provide an ordered pair that satisfies the equation of the line, and every ordered pair satisfying the linear equation are coordinates of a point on the line.

Definitions given in this chapter were:

1. *Algebra* literally means the reunion of broken parts and is that branch of mathematics which deals in the most *general* way with the operations, properties, and relations of *numbers.*

2. A *linear equation* is one that can be reduced to the form $ax + by = c$, where x and y are variables, and a, b, c are real numbers with either a or b or both not zero.

3. A *straight line* is the set of all points whose coordinates satisfy a given linear equation.

4. The *y intercept* is the point of intersection of the y axis and the given equation.

5. The *slope* of a line representing an equation in the form $y = mx + k$ is m.

6. The slope of a straight line containing the two points (x_1, x_2) and (y_1, y_2) is given by the formula

$$m = \frac{y_1 - y_2}{x_1 - x_2}$$

where $x_1 \neq x_2$.

CHAPTER REVIEW TEST ──────────────────

Find the slope, intercepts, and graph of the following equations.

1. $y - 2x = 4$
2. $\frac{1}{2}x + \frac{2}{5}y = \frac{3}{10}$
3. $3x - 2y + 3 = 2x + 3 - y$

Find the equation and graph for the following lines.

4. Having a slope of $-\frac{3}{2}$ and passing through the point $(-1, -3)$
5. Having a slope of zero and passing through the point $(4, -4)$
6. Passing through the points $(-2, -4)$ and $(-1, 1)$

Are the following statements true or false?

7. The study of algebra and the study of the real number system have very little in common.
8. The distributive property is often used in algebraic manipulation.
9. A large portion of the basic ideas and facts of algebra are learned today in grade schools.
10. If a statement is intuitively obvious then there is no need to prove it.
11. The process of graphing linear equations is over a thousand years old.

12. Who invented our system of graphically portraying relations between numbers?

13. In the equation $y = mx + k$, if $k = 5$, find the y intercept; x intercept; and slope.

14. You are to map the world on a rectangular coordinate system so that there is a one-to-one correspondence between all ordered pairs and the points on the earth:

    a. What restrictions must you impose on the set of numerals to be used for North latitudes? for South latitudes?
    b. What restrictions must you impose on the set of numerals to be used for East longitudes? for West longitudes?
    c. What other problems must you solve if you are to succeed in this mapping project? Do you suppose there is an historical parallel in the development of mathematics and the art of cartography?

CHECKING YOUR WORK

page 39

First, let us find the time spent in traveling to the city. Since we know that if we multiply the rate by the time we will obtain the distance traveled, we write $70 \cdot t = 60$, where t represents the actual number of hours spent. Solving for t, we find $t = \frac{6}{7}$ of an hour, or $\frac{6}{7} \cdot 60 = 51\frac{3}{7}$ minutes. We now consider t for the return trip: $50t = 60$, or $t = \frac{6}{5}$ hours or $\frac{6}{5} \cdot 60 = 72$ minutes spent on the return trip at 50 miles per hour. Adding these times, we find for the total trip $51\frac{3}{7} + 72 = 123\frac{3}{7}$ minutes. Since this exceeds the two-hour limitation, the intuitively developed answer of 50 miles per hour is wrong.

What did we overlook? We failed to recognize that more *time* is spent going at the slower rate than at the faster rate and, therefore, we cannot average the rates. Doing so is comparable to saying, "since I bought one can of brand A chili at 30¢ and three cans of brand *B* chili at 36¢ each, then the chili cost me an average of 33¢ a can. If you do not believe that an average of 33¢ is an erroneous conclusion, work it out with paper and pencil before you go shopping again.

We have shown that 50 miles per hour is an incorrect answer to the problem. How can we find the correct answer? Let us write down what we know. We know the total travel time is 2 hours. We know the total distance is 120 miles. But we have two rates, one of 70 miles per hour and the other an unknown rate which we call r. We have two times, one we have computed as $\frac{6}{7}$ hours consumed in driving to the city, the other an unknown time, which we again call t. But t can be computed, since we know the total time is 2 hours. Thus,

$$2 - \tfrac{6}{7} = \tfrac{8}{7} = t$$

Now, since the return trip cannot take more than $\frac{8}{7}$ hours and the distance is 60 miles, we can write for $r \cdot t = D$

$$r \cdot \tfrac{8}{7} = 60$$

If you solve this equation for r you find $r = 52.5$ miles per hour. To the nearest whole mile per hour, the correct answer is 53 miles per hour—the slowest speed you could travel to keep the total travel time at 2 hours or less.

Return to page 39

**page
46**
Again, we need to plot only two but we prefer to plot three points to draw the line described by $x = 5$. Proceeding as we did for equations in two variables, we reason as follows. If x equals 5, what must y equal? Of course, y can equal any number and it does not change or affect the equation $x = 5$. Suppose y equals 7, what must x equal? The answer, of course, is 5. Thus, we have the ordered pair (5, 7). If y is -3, x still equals 5, and we have the ordered pair (5, -3). So we say x equals 5 for all values of y and draw the line as shown below. This line is the set of points $\{(5, y)|y \in R\}$, because all such ordered pairs satisfy the equation $x = 5$ (see Figure 2-7).

Return to page 46

**page
47**
Problem 5: Multiplying the equation by 6, we have

$2x - 3y = 6y$ or $2x + (-9y) = 0$

Here $a = 2$, $b = -9$, and $c = 0$.

Problem 7: Multiplying the equation by x, we have

**Figure
2-7**

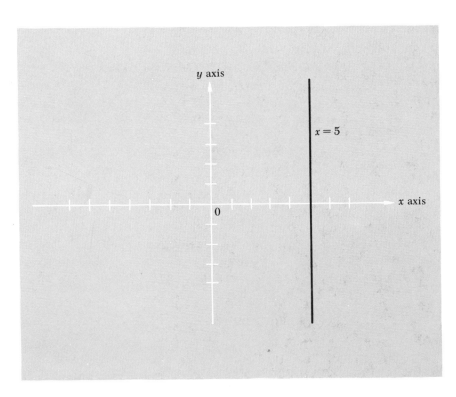

$\frac{1}{2} - \frac{1}{4} = 4x$ or $4x + 0y = \frac{1}{4}$

where $a = 4$, $b = 0$, and $c = \frac{1}{4}$.

Return to page 47

page 47
Ordinarily, we find one y intercept. The two exceptions to this rule occur when the coefficient of y is zero in the general linear equation. Such an equation takes the form of $ax + 0y = c$. The first exception occurs when $c = 0$. We note that x must also equal zero, while y can equal any value. Thus the solution set of ordered pairs is $\{(0, y)|y \in R\}$, and the plotted line is the y axis itself. Here, no unique y intercept can be defined, because every point on the y axis is a y intercept. The second exception occurs when $c \neq 0$. In this case, we note that x must be equal to the constant c/a, while y again may have any value. Hence, this equation is represented by a vertical line parallel to the y axis and has *no* y intercept. However, in all other cases there is only one y intercept for any linear equation. Test this last statement with the equation $0x + by = c$.

Return to page 47

page 48
The graph of any linear equation solved for y that has a negative coefficient of x "runs downhill." When the coefficient of x is positive, the line "runs uphill." Notice in Figure 2-3 that as the value of y decreases, the value of x must, of necessity, increase.

Return to page 48

page 52
The graph in Figure 2-5 shows that when $x = 0$, y must be -3. But in our equation of $y = -3x + k$, if $x = 0$, then $y = k$; and if y equals -3, then k must equal -3. To check this value of k, let $y = 0$. We then have $0 = -3x + (-3)$ or $3x = -3$ or $x = -1$. This value of x (when $y = 0$) is confirmed by Figure 2-5. We now can write $y = -3x - 3$, the equation graphed in Figure 2-5.

Return to page 52

3

QUADRATIC EQUATIONS

A review of exponents as well as of the vocabulary used will prove helpful in our discussion of some nonlinear algebraic equations. If any part of this discussion covers new material for you rather than being a review of things you have learned before, you are urged to supplement these two sections with outside readings and related exercises, which you can find in any standard algebra text.

3.1   Vocabulary

Monomial

A monomial is a single algebraic term such as x, $-3x$, $-\frac{2}{3}xy$, or $\sqrt{2} \cdot z^5$. A monomial can be a constant, a variable, or a product of any combination of these.

Binomial

A binomial is the sum of exactly two monomials, such as $2x + \frac{3}{2}xy$.

Trinomial

A trinomial is the sum of exactly three monomials, such as $3x^2 - ax + 3$.

Polynomial

A polynomial is a sum of monomials. Polynomials are also often referred to as compound expressions—algebraic expressions having two or more terms.

Linear Polynomial

A linear polynomial in one variable can always be expressed in standard form as $ax + b$, where x is the variable, a and b are real numbers, and $a \neq 0$. If a were zero, the expression would be reduced to a monomial. Since the variable is to the first power only, a linear polynomial is also known as a *first-degree polynomial.*

Quadratic

A quadratic in one variable can always be expressed by the collection of similar terms in the standard form of $ax^2 + bx + c$, where a, b, c are real numbers, x is the variable, and $a \neq 0$. A quadratic is another name for a *second-degree polynomial.*

Third-Degree Polynomial

A third-degree polynomial (or *cubic*) in one variable can always be expressed in the standard form of $ax^3 + bx^2 + cx + d$, where all the coefficients are real numbers, and $a \neq 0$.

Let us examine one of the above definitions more closely. The definition of a linear polynomial states that any linear polynomial can be expressed in the standard form of $ax + b$. This fact results from the closure property of addition over the set of real numbers. For example,

$3x + 17 + (-7x) + 3 + (-22) + 6x$

certainly meets the definition of a linear polynomial in one variable. This expression can be simplified by combining similar terms through the application of the properties of the real numbers as follows

$3x + (-7x) + 6x + 17 + 3 + (-22)$ (commuting)
$2x + (-2)$ (associating, distributing, and adding)

The polynomial is now in the standard form, where $a = 2$, $b = -2$. We know from our study of the real numbers that the difference of two numbers is equal to the sum of the first and the additive inverse of the second. However, when we simplify polynomials, we write $2x - 2$ rather than $2x + (-2)$, because the former is simpler to write.

The degree of any polynomial in one variable is the highest power to which the variable is raised. For example,

$$ax^0 + cx^7 + gx^9$$

is a polynomial of degree 9, $a \neq 0$. Of course, many of the terms are "missing" because their coefficients are zero. Similarly, a polynomial in two variables such as

$$x^7 y^5 + x^3 y^4 + 3xy$$

is of degree 7 in x and of degree 5 in y; but if we do not specify the variable, the polynomial is of degree 12. (Suppose $x = y$.)

3.2   Review of Exponents

We have agreed that a representation like a^2 means $a \cdot a$, b^3 means $b \cdot b \cdot b$, where we speak of "b cubed," "b raised to the third power," or "the third power of b." We call b the "base" and 3 the "exponent." This language and system of notation was suggested by Descartes and provides a convenient shorthand for writing the product of a number used as a factor a great number of times. As a result we can write $a \cdot a \cdot a \cdot a \cdot b \cdot b \cdot b$ as $a^4 b^3$.

We also note that $a^2 a^3 = (a \cdot a) \cdot (a \cdot a \cdot a)$. Because of the associative property we can write this as $a \cdot a \cdot a \cdot a \cdot a$, which equals a^5. By the transitive property of equals, then, $a^2 a^3 = a^5$. This leads to

$$a^m a^n = a^{m+n}$$

where a is any real number and m and n are positive integers.

Let us prove this to be true. By definition, we can write

$$a^m a^n = \underbrace{(a \cdot a \cdot a \cdots a)}_{m \text{ times}} \cdot \underbrace{(a \cdot a \cdot a \cdots a)}_{n \text{ times}}$$

$$= \underbrace{a \cdot a \cdot a \cdots a}_{m \text{ times}} \cdot \underbrace{a \cdot a \cdot a \cdots a}_{n \text{ times}}$$

The last expression was obtained by the associative property of multiplication and represents the product of a taken exactly $m + n$ times. By definition, we again write this as a^{m+n}. Thus $a^m a^n = a^{m+n}$ for any real number a raised to powers m, n (elements of C).

Can we simplify an algebraic term like a^m/a^n? Let us write it out.

$$\frac{a^m}{a^n} = \frac{\overbrace{a \cdot a \cdot a \cdots a}^{m \text{ times}}}{\underbrace{a \cdot a \cdot a \cdots a}_{n \text{ times}}}$$

Assuming $m > n$, we divide out each a in the denominator and a given number of a's remain in the numerator. Try it until you are convinced that the number of a's is $m - n$. Now we know that $a^m/a^n = a^{m-n}$. But here we assumed $m > n$. According to the trichotomy property, two other possibilities exist: $m = n$ and $m < n$.

Assume $m = n$. Now each a in the denominator can be put into one-to-one correspondence with each a in the numerator. When we divide out the a's, we have left a series of products of one; thus for $m = n$, $a^m/a^n = 1$. In keeping with our earlier result $a^m/a^n = a^{m-n}$, if $m = n$ then $a^m/a^n = a^{m-n} = a^0$, which as we have just shown equals one. Since all of our work so far required exponents that were counting numbers, i.e., positive integers, we are led to define a^0 as being equal to one.

We are saying that *any* real number (except zero) raised to the zeroth power equals 1. For example,

$$48^0 = 1 \qquad (x^2yz^3)^0 = 1 \qquad \left(\frac{2a^3b}{3ab^2}\right)^0 = 1$$

Our definition is logical because the only way we can obtain a zero exponent is when the factors in the numerator and denominator of a fraction are exactly equal. For example,

$$\frac{48^9}{48^9} = \frac{48 \cdot 48 \cdot 48 \cdot 48 \cdot 48 \cdot 48 \cdot 48 \cdot 48 \cdot 48}{48 \cdot 48 \cdot 48 \cdot 48 \cdot 48 \cdot 48 \cdot 48 \cdot 48 \cdot 48}$$
$$= 1 \cdot 1 \cdot 1 \cdot 1 \cdot 1 \cdot 1 \cdot 1 \cdot 1 \cdot 1 = 1$$

We can now save space by writing

$$\frac{48^9}{48^9} = 48^{9-9} = 48^0 = 1$$

Note that if the base had been any number other than 48 (except zero), the final answer would still have been 1. Can you explain to a fellow student's satisfaction why zero is excluded as a base?

Now assume $m < n$. Each a in the numerator is divided out by an a in the denominator and a whole number of a's are left in the denominator. To illustrate, let $m = 3$ and $n = 5$. Then

$$\frac{a^m}{a^n} = \frac{a^3}{a^5} = \frac{a \cdot a \cdot a}{a \cdot a \cdot a \cdot a \cdot a} = \frac{1}{a \cdot a} = \frac{1}{a^2}$$

For the cases where $m = n$ and $m > n$, we note that $a^m/a^n = a^{m-n}$. Using this formula, with $m < n$, we obtain

$$\frac{a^3}{a^5} = a^{3-5} = a^{-2}$$

So if we define $a^{-2} = 1/a^2$, the general law holds for all three cases, and $a^m/a^n = a^{m-n}$ for any real number a $(a \neq 0)$, and any integers m, n, and k, where a^{-k} is defined to be $1/a^k$.

Using this law we can simplify $a^{-3} \cdot a^4 \cdot a^0 \cdot a^{-2}$ as $a^{-3+4+0-2} = a^{-1} = 1/a$. Or, depending on the form of the problem and the desired form of the simplification, we might have

$$\frac{a^4 a^0}{a^3 a^2} = \frac{a^4}{a^{3+2}} = \frac{a^4}{a^5} = \frac{1}{a} = a^{-1}$$

Another common expression to consider involves raising a power to a power. For example, what does $(a^3)^2$ mean? By the definition of the exponent we know it means $(a \cdot a \cdot a)^2$, which in turn means $(a \cdot a \cdot a) \cdot (a \cdot a \cdot a)$, or, by the associative property, $a \cdot a \cdot a \cdot a \cdot a \cdot a = a^6$. Does this mean we can generalize and say $(a^m)^n$ equals $a^{m \cdot n}$ for all integers m and n? Let us see if we can show this to be the case.

Using the same procedure and notation as before, we can write

$$(a^m)^n = \underbrace{(a \cdot a \cdot a \cdots a)}_{m \text{ times}}{}^n$$

$$= \underbrace{\underbrace{(a \cdot a \cdot a \cdots a)}_{m \text{ times}} \cdot \underbrace{(a \cdot a \cdot a \cdots a)}_{m \text{ times}} \cdots \underbrace{(a \cdot a \cdot a \cdots a)}_{m \text{ times}}}_{n \text{ times}}$$

But this equals exactly n *times* m number of a's. Thus $(a^m)^n$ is equivalent to $a^{m \cdot n}$ for any real number a raised to the integral powers m and n. (Note that if either m or $n = 0$, the result is 1.)

Finally, we recall that

$$\left(\frac{a}{b}\right)^n = \frac{a^n}{b^n} = a^n b^{-n}$$

for all integers a, b, n, $b \neq 0$. Also $(a \cdot b)^n = a^n \cdot b^n$. Notice that here the base numbers are *different*. Common errors made in manipulating exponential forms result from the student attempting to apply the laws discussed here when the bases are different. For example, $(2x)^2 = 4x^2$ and *not* $2x^2$. Similarly, $a^m/b^n \neq (ab)^{m-n}$, but rather $a^m b^{-n}$.

Laws of Exponents

We summarize the laws of exponents as follows. For any real numbers a, b (not zero) and integers m and n,

1. $a^m a^n = a^{m+n}$ 5. $(a^m)^n = a^{m \cdot n}$

2. $\dfrac{a^m}{a^n} = a^{m-n}$ 6. $\left(\dfrac{a}{b}\right)^m = \dfrac{a^m}{b^m} = a^m b^{-m}$

3. $a^0 = 1$ 7. $(a \cdot b)^m = a^m b^m$

4. $\dfrac{1}{a^m} = a^{-m}$

Because so much time is wasted due to careless or erroneous applications of these laws, you are urged to practice their use until you have achieved a high degree of skill. Memorization of these laws is helpful for this course, but it does not replace the acquisition of an understanding and the ability to derive them. This ability should be accessible after the memorized formulas have been forgotten.

EXERCISES
3.2

Simplify the following expressions (if possible).

1. $2a^2$

2. $(2a)^2$

3. $3(2a)^2$

4. $x^4 x^{-3}$

5. $x^3 y^{-2} x^2 y^2$

6. $\dfrac{2^3 \cdot 2^0}{2}$

7. $\dfrac{2^{-7} \cdot 2^5}{2^{-2}(2^{-4})^0}$

8. $(3a^2)^2$

9. $\dfrac{(2a^2)^3 \cdot 2b^2}{8a^4 \cdot b^2}$

10. $\dfrac{-2(3a)^2}{(-3a)^3}$

11. $\dfrac{-3(2a^2 + b)^0 + 3}{2a^3(b^2)^3 \cdot (-3b)^2}$

12. $[x(-2x)^2]^3$

13. $\dfrac{a(3b^2)^2 - (-b)^3}{a^3 - b^2}$

14. $\dfrac{3b(a + b) + 6a + 6b}{(a - b)^0(a + b)}$

15. $\dfrac{[-(-2a)^2]^3 + 8a^3}{(-4)(-a)^3}$

16. The enterprising student should develop a rationale for working with m and n as elements of Ra rather than being restricted

to I. Try to develop proofs for the exponent laws given previously on page 70 if m, $n \in Ra$.

(Hint: $\sqrt{4} = (4)^{1/2}$, by definition, and $\sqrt[2]{a} = a^{1/2}$ and $\sqrt[2]{a^3} = a^{3/2}$.)

3.3 Graphing

We are now prepared to develop some concepts about nonlinear equations. Once again, our graphing skills prove valuable in the development of these concepts.

We have seen that we can represent a linear equation graphically. We have also seen that this representation is always a straight line with its slope dependent upon the constants of the equation. Can you draw the graph of a nonlinear equation? Consider, for example,

$$y = x^2 \tag{1}$$

This equation does not meet the criteria for a linear equation, since one of the variables is raised to the second power. Because the highest power here is 2, this is a quadratic equation in x.

Using our system of Cartesian coordinates, let us plot several points whose coordinates would satisfy equation (1). Let us compute for several different values of x the resultant values of y. If $x = 0$, y must be zero also. Following this pattern, you should confirm that for each x the corresponding value of y is the one indicated in the table.

x	0	1	2	3	−1	−2	−3
y	0	1	4	9	1	4	9

Next we plot the set of points corresponding to

$$\{(0, 0), (1, 1), (2, 4), (3, 9), (-1, 1), (-2, 4), (-3, 9)\}$$

in Figure 3-1.

Clearly, the equation satisfied by the coordinates of these points is not a linear equation because the points are not collinear. The points appear, however, to have some symmetry about them. Let us plot additional points between the values of $x = 1$ and $x = 2$.

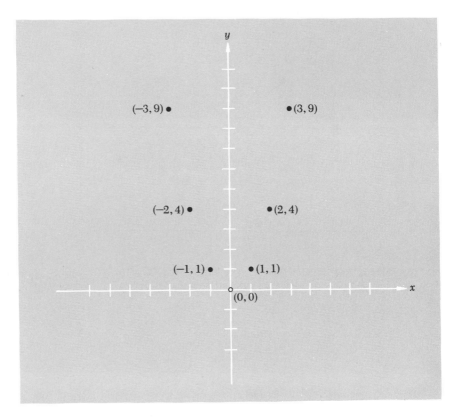

Figure 3-1

x	1.1	1.2	1.3	1.4	1.5	1.6	1.7	1.8	1.9
y	1.21	1.44	1.69	1.96	2.25	2.56	2.89	3.24	3.61

If we computed enough of these we would soon conclude that for every small change in the value assigned to x, we would obtain a small change in the value of y. The smaller the change in x, the smaller the change in y,[1] and the closer together would be the plotted points, until they would blend into a smooth curve as shown in Figures 3-2 and 3-3.

---

[1] This type of reasoning brings us to the verge of differential calculus, another part of mathematics, which is simply an extension of *thinking using a number system*. You may recall that both Leibnitz and Newton independently developed differential calculus and that there was some controversy among followers of both men regarding who had been the true "inventor." Still others believe Pierre de Fermat, a French lawyer whose hobby was mathematics, was the inventor of differential calculus. You are encouraged to read about the many accomplishments of this amateur, sometimes known as the greatest "co-inventor" in mathematics.

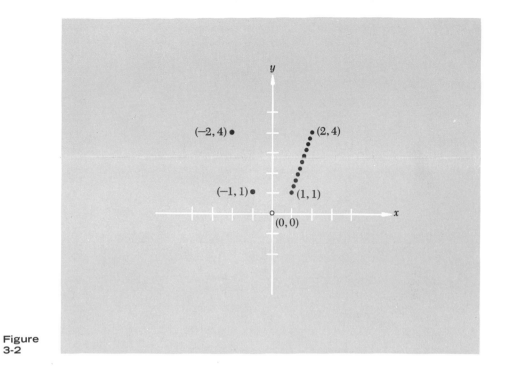

**Figure
3-2**

**Figure
3-3**

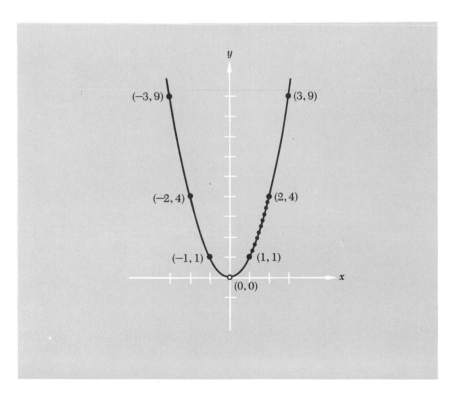

This supports the hypothesis that all the coordinates satisfying equation (1) define points on the curve represented in Figure 3-3. Conversely, we can state that the coordinates identifying any point on the curve satisfy equation (1).

To convince yourself of the truth of the above statement, plot a sufficient number of points to enable you to draw a smooth curve of the following quadratic equations:

$2y = 2x^2$	(1)	$y = x^2 + 4x + 4$	(6)
$y = x^2 + 4$	(2)	$y = x^2 - 4x + 4$	(7)
$y = x^2 - 4$	(3)	$y = x^2 + 2x - 8$	(8)
$y = x^2 + 4x$	(4)	$y = x^2 - 4x + 8$	(9)
$y = x^2 - 4x$	(5)		

All of the graphs of equations (1)–(9) are similar. Curves of this type are called *parabolas*. You may recall from your previous work that the lowest point of each of these curves is called the *vertex* of the parabola. You should notice by inspection of your drawings for equations (4)–(9) that the vertex is not always at the same point. Can you determine from your graphs the condition necessary for the vertex to coincide with the y intercept? Curves (1)–(3) are said to be symmetric with respect to the y axis. Check your graphs against those given in Figure 3-4.

Notice that curves (6) and (7) are congruent, but that curve (7) has been shifted four units to the right along the x axis. By examining equations (6) and (7), what can you conclude about the cause of this translation?

What is the significance of the x intercepts in the graphs? Ponder this question, formulate your conclusion, and

CHECK YOUR WORK on page 110

When y is set equal to zero, x can have no more than two possible values in such equations. Judging from their graphs in Figure 3-4, equations (2) and (9) apparently have no solutions in the set of real numbers for $y = 0$. This can be confirmed by studying equations (2) and (9). In equation (2), when $y = 0$, we have $x^2 + 4 = 0$. Adding the

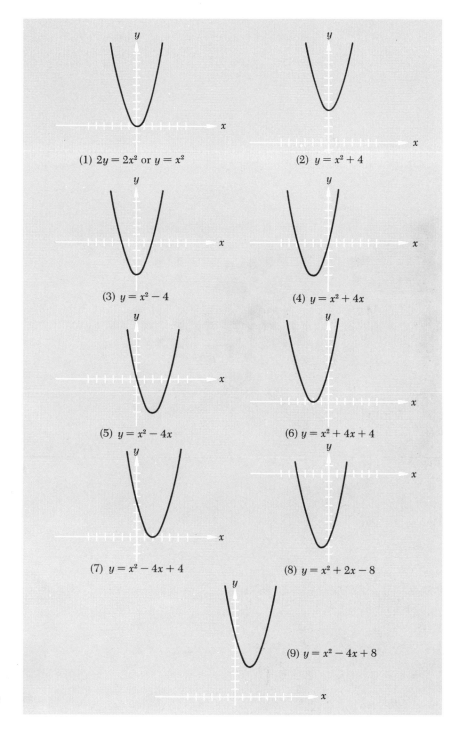

(1) $2y = 2x^2$ or $y = x^2$

(2) $y = x^2 + 4$

(3) $y = x^2 - 4$

(4) $y = x^2 + 4x$

(5) $y = x^2 - 4x$

(6) $y = x^2 + 4x + 4$

(7) $y = x^2 - 4x + 4$

(8) $y = x^2 + 2x - 8$

(9) $y = x^2 - 4x + 8$

Figure 3-4

additive inverse to each side, we obtain $x^2 = -4$. Next we search for some real number, which when multiplied by itself yields -4. Such elements we call *roots*. However, for equation (2) we find no such number. Equation (2) has no real roots. It is precisely this kind of failure in seeking closure under a given operation that will later motivate us (as it has before) to add still another set of numbers to the set of real numbers.

The nine equations pictured in Figure 3-4 were selected to demonstrate the observations regarding translation, x intercepts, and lack of real roots. You should realize that parabolas do not always open upwards. For example, examine the parabolas you obtain when you draw the graphs of the following two quadratic equations:

$$x = y^2 \qquad (10) \qquad\qquad\qquad x^2 = -y \qquad (11)$$

If you did your work correctly, your graphs should look like those shown in Figure 3-5.

However, our purpose here is not to study parabolas, but to demonstrate that nonlinear equations in two variables can be graphed— to gain an understanding of the relationships between graphs and equations, and to show that we can tell a great deal about a graph from its equation.

Let us look briefly at another possibility. Suppose two variables in an equation are each raised to the second power. Consider

Figure 3-5

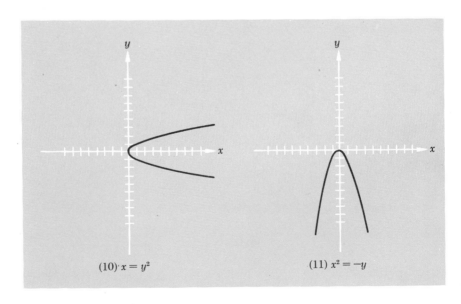

(10)$' x = y^2$ (11) $x^2 = -y$

$x^2 + y^2 = 25$

Can the graph of this equation be drawn?

Again, we try to find the value of x when y is zero. We obtain two roots, $x = +5$ and $x = -5$. Similarly, if $x = 0$, we find that $y = +5$ and $y = -5$. If we continue this process, a table of corresponding values can be developed as follows:

x	0	0	5	−5	3	3	−3	−3	4	4	−4	−4	2	1
y	5	−5	0	0	4	−4	4	−4	3	−3	3	−3	$\sqrt{21}$	$\sqrt{24}$

When the points corresponding to the ordered pairs (x, y) in the table are plotted on Cartesian coordinates as in Figure 3-6, we find that the set of coordinates satisfying the equation forms the locus of a circle of radius 5.

Figure 3-6

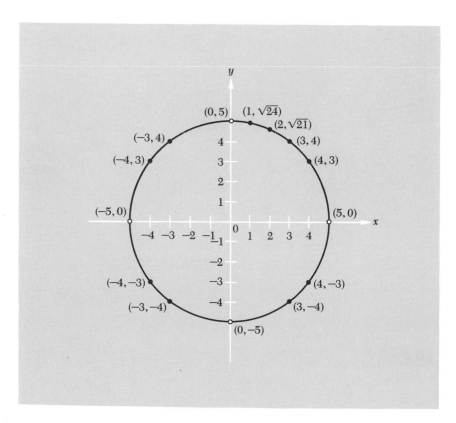

This example illustrates the fact that nonlinear equations in two variables can also be represented graphically. With some exceptions ($x^2 = 4$, for example), all quadratics generate curves in the ordinary sense of the word, and much can be predicted about these curves from their equations. Conversely, much can also be predicted about an equation from its graph.

EXERCISES
3.3

Draw the graph of each of the following

1.	$y = x^2 - 3$	4.	$x^2 + y^2 = 16$
2.	$-x = y^2$	5.	$4x^2 + y^2 = 36$
3.	$y = x^2 + 2x - 2$	6.	$y = x^3 - x$

By inspecting each of the following equations, tell whether its graph is a circle, parabola, or a straight line.

7.	$y = x^2$	11.	$y = x - 3 + x^2$
8.	$y = x + 3$	12.	$x^2 - 36 + y^2 = 0$
9.	$7x - 14 = 5x - 2y$	13.	$(3x)^2 + y^2 = 0$
10.	$x^2 + 3x - 7x^2 = y$	14.	$12x^2 - 3y^2 - 8x^2 = 4 - 5y^2$

3.4 The Greek Solution

We will return to our discussion of graphs and their relationship to equations later. At this point we must pause to consider in greater detail the quadratic equations, which occupy an important place in the study of algebra.

There are many rules for the solution of quadratic equations, and we must therefore be careful throughout the remainder of this chapter not to lose sight of the reasons behind these rules. Our aim is to achieve the skills necessary to *solve* "everyday" problems and to gain a better appreciation of the power of algebraic methods.

Mathematics has been invented because of the need to measure, and the need to find meaningful answers to some problem. To the Greeks, all problems were measurement problems. A quadratic equation such as $x^2 + 2x = 35$ was the mathematical description of an area the total size of which was 35. The area may have been composed of a square of sides x plus a rectangle of sides 2 and x, or simply of a rectangle with sides x and $x + 2$. In either case, they determined the length of x by a mechanism termed *completing the square*. They drew a square with sides x and then, instead of drawing a rectangle of sides x and 2, they would draw two figures of sides 1 and x as shown in Figure 3-7.

The area required to complete the larger square is obvious when the problem is illustrated in this manner. In this case, of course, the "added" area is one times one, or one square unit. The area of the original three sections was given by the equation to be 35; therefore, the area of the "completed" square is $1 + 35 = 36$. Hence the sides of the completed square must each be 6. But each side is seen to be $x + 1$, so that $x + 1$ must equal 6, and x must be 5. Substituting this value of x into the original equation, we find it to be correct.

Apply this "completing the square" method to the following equations:

$x^2 + 10x = 39$	(1)	$x^2 - 4x = 12$	(4)
$9x^2 + 6x = 48$	(2)	$x^2 + 3x = 4$	(5)
$2x^2 + 4x = 70$	(3)	$x^2 - 6x = 7$	(6)

Figure 3-7

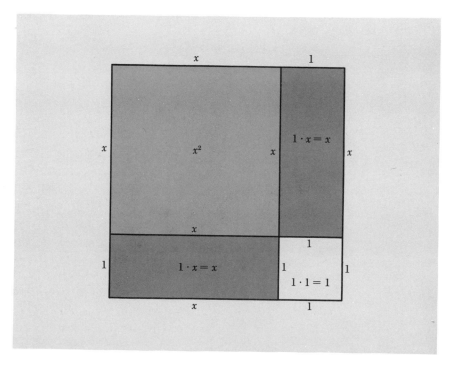

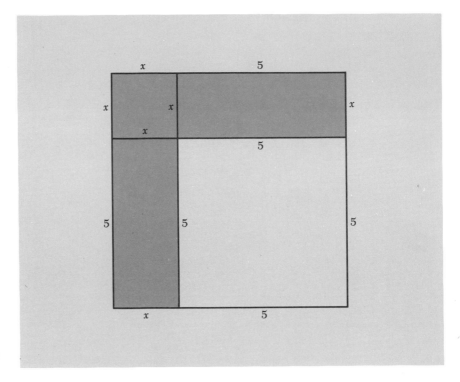

Figure 3-8

You should notice that each of these exercises presents a different type of problem. These exercises were devised to point out to you what might easily have been the thought pattern involved in the development of solutions to such problems. For example, in equation (1) the coefficient of x^2 is one and the coefficient of x is an even number. In equation (2) the coefficient of x^2 is not one, but is the square of a counting number. If you can solve these problems, can you also solve one with a coefficient of x^2 that is not the square of a counting number, for example, equation (3)? Can you solve an equation of this type if the coefficient of x is negative or an odd number?

Your drawing for problem 1 might well look like Figure 3-8, where the shaded area represents x^2 plus $5x$ plus $5x$, or $x^2 + 10x$, which by equation (1) equals 39. To complete the square we have added a 5 by 5 section, which has an area of 25. The total area of the new square is then $39 + 25 = 64$, and since $8^2 = 64$, each side must be 8. But the sides of the new square are $x + 5$, so $x + 5$ must equal 8 and $x = 3$. Substituting in the original equation, we find $3^2 + 10 \cdot 3 = 9 + 30 = 39$. Do problems 2–6 and then

CHECK YOUR WORK on page 110

If you followed the method given in the solution to problem 4, consider another method using the Cartesian coordinate system. Plot the areas given in the equation $x^2 - 4x = 12$ and "complete the square."

From the origin $(0,0)$ mark off a distance of $+x$ on the x axis and a distance of $+x$ on the y axis and connect these points with the point (x, x) to obtain a square of sides x with vertices at $(0,0)$, $(x, 0)$, $(0, x)$, (x, x), as shown in Figure 3-9. Now draw a rectangle of area $2x$ by connecting $(0, 0)$, $(-2, 0)$, $(0, x)$, and $(-2, x)$. Draw a second rectangle of equal size by connecting $(0,0)$, $(x, 0)$, $(0, -2)$, and $(x, -2)$. Finally, complete the large square by connecting $(-2, 0)$ with $(-2, -2)$ and $(-2, -2)$ with $(0, -2)$.

The completed square has sides $-2 + x$ or $x - 2$. But the unshaded area in Figure 3-9 is $x^2 - 4x$, which is given equal to 12 in the equation. The shaded area is seen to be $(-2) \cdot (-2)$ or 4. Thus the total area of the large square is $12 + 4$ or 16 so each side must equal 4. But each

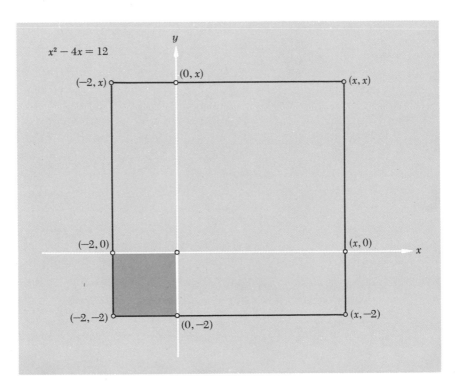

Figure
3-9

side is also $x - 2$, so we can write $x - 2 = 4$ and find that $x = 6$. Will this procedure work for problem 6? Can you see an advantage to this procedure over the first method presented?

3.5 Factoring

By now you should appreciate the difficulty in solving some of the area problems in the manner presented. You probably recall from your high school algebra that there are other ways of solving such equations. Factoring skills are important in the use of these methods.

We already know that factoring numbers into their prime factors is often useful in verifying that two numbers are relatively prime, in determining whether or not a fraction is reduced, and in finding the least common multiple of two or more numbers. We shall see that factoring is even more valuable in algebra.

In algebra, much of the value of factoring stems from the fact that we are dealing with variables, or literal numbers, for which we are seeking the solution set. This aspect makes one of the properties of zero of great value. We recall that if the product of two numbers is zero, then at least one of the numbers must be zero. Hence, if we can factor an algebraic expression after setting it equal to zero, then the product of the factors is zero, and we can capitalize on this property. For example, if $x^2 + x = 0$, then $x(x + 1) = 0$, and either $x = 0$ or $x + 1 = 0$. You may recall most of your factoring skills acquired in high school, but you should note that the easiest way to determine "how to factor" in algebra is first to understand "how to multiply."

When we multiply $a \cdot (a - 3)$, we use the distributive property and obtain $a^2 - 3a$. Looking at this problem in the reverse order, we notice that each term in $a^2 - 3a$ has a common factor a, which we can "factor out" because of the *distributive property* and write $a \cdot (a - 3)$.

Similarly, when we find the product of $(a + 2) \cdot (a - 3)$, we distribute the number $(a + 2)$ across the difference $(a - 3)$ and obtain $(a + 2) \cdot a - (a + 2) \cdot 3$. Again applying the distributive property, we distribute the a across $(a + 2)$ and the 3 across $(a + 2)$ and find $a^2 + 2a - 3a - 6$. Combining similar terms, we have $a^2 - a - 6$. This repetitive application of the distributive property is generally shortened by using some sort of "rule" to speed the multiplication process.

One common rule used is the "means and extremes rule." It states that the product of two binomials, such as $(a + 2)(a - 3)$, is equal to the product of their first terms $(a \cdot a)$ plus the sum of the products of the mean terms and the extreme terms $(2 \cdot a) + (-3 \cdot a)$ plus the product of the end terms $(2 \cdot (-3))$. To illustrate

$$\overset{\text{means}}{(a + \overbrace{2)(a} - 3)} = a^2 + \{2a + (-3a)\} - 6 = a^2 - a - 6$$
$$\underbrace{}_{\text{extremes}}$$

Note the natural merging of arithmetic into algebra in the structure of such rules. The "means and extremes rule" is in exact correspondence with the common multiplication algorithm used in elementary school work. When we multiply 28 times 67 we commonly proceed as follows:

$$
\begin{array}{r}
28 \\
67 \\
\hline
196 \\
168 \\
\hline
1876
\end{array}
\tag{1}
$$

This is a short form of

$$
\begin{array}{r}
28 \\
67 \\
\hline
56 \\
140 \\
480 \\
1200 \\
\hline
1876
\end{array}
\tag{2}
$$

In expanded form the problem is $(2 \cdot 10 + 8) \cdot (6 \cdot 10 + 7)$ and we could write

$$
\begin{array}{r}
2 \cdot 10 + 8 \\
6 \cdot 10 + 7 \\
\hline
56 \\
14 \cdot 10 \\
48 \cdot 10 \\
12 \cdot 10 \cdot 10 \\
\hline
56 \\
140 \\
480 \\
1200 \\
\hline
1876
\end{array}
\tag{3}
$$

To save space we could follow the "means and extremes rule" and say $(2 \cdot 10 + 8) \cdot (6 \cdot 10 + 7)$ equals:

[the product of the first terms $(2 \cdot 10)(6 \cdot 10)$] $= 1200$

$$\text{plus} \begin{bmatrix} \text{the sum of the product of:} \\ \text{the means} \quad (8 \cdot 6 \cdot 10) = \quad 480 \\ \text{the extremes} \quad (2 \cdot 10 \cdot 7) = +140 \\ \overline{620} \end{bmatrix} = \quad 620$$

plus [the product of the end terms $(8 \cdot 7)$] $= + \quad \underline{56}$
                                                          1876

So $(20 + 8) \cdot (60 + 7)$ is equal to 1876.

Let us solve another problem in a shorter manner than usual, capitalizing on this rule.

$$(34)(45) = (30 + 4)(40 + 5) = 1200 + (160 + 150) + 20 = 1530$$

Using the regular multiplication algorithm, we have

$$
\begin{array}{c}
34 \\
\underline{45} \\
170 \\
136 \\
\hline
1530
\end{array}
\qquad \text{which means} \qquad
\begin{array}{c}
34 \\
\underline{45} \\
20 \\
\left.\begin{array}{c} 150 \\ 160 \end{array}\right\} \; 15 \cdot 10 + 16 \cdot 10 = 310 \\
\underline{1200} \\
1530
\end{array}
$$

Note that we are summing the same three numbers, $20 + 310 + 1200$.

We find our regular multiplication algorithm more advantageous in arithmetic because we know the value of the numbers to be multiplied. In algebra, however, we deal with literal numbers and cannot simplify the algorithm so extensively. Similarities can be seen if we study the following:

$$
\begin{array}{ccc}
(a + 2) & 40 + 2 & 40 + 2 \\
\underline{(a - 3)} & \underline{40 - 3} & \underline{30 + 7} \\
-6 & -6 & 14 \\
-3a & -3(40) & 280 \\
+2a & +2(40) & 60 \\
\underline{a^2} & \underline{(40)^2} & \underline{1200} \\
a^2 - a - 6 & 40^2 - 40 - 6 & 1554
\end{array}
$$

$$1600 - 46 = 1554$$

Often the products of the means and extremes can be summed mentally when they are given in similar terms. Space is saved by writing $(a + 2)(a - 3) = a^2 - a - 6$ through mental application of the rule. The "means and extremes rule" is nothing more than the best multiplication algorithm we have invented for speeding the process of multiplying two binomials—just as our usual multiplication algorithm in arithmetic is the best we have invented for speeding the process in arithmetic.

Consider $(x + 1)(x + 3)$. Applying the rule, we multiply mentally and write the answer of $x^2 + 4x + 3$. Suppose $x = 20$. Our answer indicates the value would be $(20 \cdot 20) + 4 \cdot 20 + 3 = 400 + 80 + 3 = 483$. If we substituted for x in the original problem, we would find $(20 + 1)(20 + 3) = 21 \cdot 23$ or 483. Writing out both algebraic and arithmetic solutions shows the correspondence between the two algorithms.

$$
\begin{array}{ll}
23 & x + 3 \\
\underline{21} & \underline{x + 1} \\
3 \longrightarrow \quad 3 \longleftarrow \quad & -3 \\
\left.\begin{array}{r}20 \\ 60\end{array}\right\} \longrightarrow \quad 80 \longleftarrow \left\{\begin{array}{l} x \\ 3x \end{array}\right. \\
\underline{400} \longrightarrow 400 \longleftarrow \underline{\quad x^2} \\
483 & x^2 + 4x + 3
\end{array}
$$

The reverse process $(400 + 80 + 3)$ is that of finding the factors of a number. In arithmetic, we factor by dividing out one factor at a time, each determined by inspection. (See Chapter 1, page 19.) In algebra, we also factor on the basis of a reasoned inspection of the number to be factored. We know that if a quadratic can be factored into two binomials of the first degree, it must take certain forms.

We know from our work above, for example, that if we factor $x^2 + 3x - 28$, it takes the form of $(x \quad)(x \quad)$. We know the product of the end terms must be -28 and their sum must be 3. (How do we know this?) One end term must be negative, the other positive. (Why?) Only three pairs of integers exist whose product is 28. They are $(1, 28)$, $(2, 14)$, and $(4, 7)$. We find by inspection that the only one of the three pairs having a difference of 3 is $(4, 7)$. Since their sum must be positive, the larger integer is the positive number. Thus, the factors we are looking for are $(x + 7)(x - 4)$.

To illustrate how we can capitalize on the zero property in solving quadratic equations, let us assume a problem has been converted to the equation $x^2 + 3x = 28$. Adding the additive inverse of 28 to both members of the equation, we obtain $x^2 + 3x - 28 = 0$. We have already found the factors of the left-hand side of the equation, and can thus write $(x + 7)(x - 4) = 0$. Now, since at least one of the two factors must be equal to zero, since their product is zero, either $x + 7 = 0$, or $x - 4 = 0$. Both of these yield real solutions of the equation. Solving each possibility, we find $x = -7$, or $x = 4$. But assume for the moment that this problem was originally an area problem as seen by the Greeks, then the -7 answer is meaningless and 4 is the answer we would be seeking. (Check both solutions in the original equation.)

Now work the above problem this time using the method of drawing rectangles, and compare the work and difficulty of the two methods.

Notice that if an equation takes the form $a^2 - 3a = 0$, factoring provides a quick method of solution. Identifying and extracting a factor or factors common to all terms is the easiest type of factoring and should always be attempted as a first step. Thus $a^2 - 3a = a(a - 3) = 0$; therefore, $a = 0$, or $a - 3 = 0$. The solution set of the equation has been found as $\{0, 3\}$. Does each member of the solution set satisfy the original equation?

See if you can apply the ideas we have discussed in this brief discussion in the following exercises. If, after doing all of these, you are still not confident in the method of factoring, invest some hours with a friend working similar problems. Many such problems can be found in any beginning algebra text.

EXERCISES
3.5

Multiply the following factors.

1. $(x + 9)(x - 3)$
2. $(x - 2)(x + 5)$
3. $(x - 7)(x - 4)$
4. $(x + 5)(x + 5)$
5. $(2x - 3)(3x + 5)$
6. $(xy - 7)(xy + 7)$
7. $(x^2 - y)(x^2 + 3y)$
8. $x(x - 2)(x + 3)$

Factor the following expressions.

9. $x^2 + 11x + 28$
10. $x^2 + 6x - 27$
11. $x^2 - x - 20$
12. $xy^2 + 3xy + 2x$
13. $2x^2 + 7x + 3$
14. $6x^2 + 7xy - 3y^2$
15. $x^2y^2 - 7xy + 6$
16. $9x^2 - 24x + 16$
17. $x^2 + 2x - 63$
18. $2a^3b - 4a^2b - 70ab$
19. $4a^2 - 28a - 72$
20. $18a^2b - 27ab^2 + 36a^2b$

Solve for x in the following equations, and check your answers in the original equation.

21. $x^2 + 5x + 6 = 0$ 25. $x^2 - 9 = 0$
22. $x^2 - 3x + 2 = 0$ 26. $42ax^2 + 6a = 48ax$
23. $x^2 = 9x - 20$ 27. $6x = 2x^2$
24. $x(2x - 5) = 42$ 28. $15a + 7a - 16ax - 3a = 4a - ax^2$

3.6 Applications of Factoring in Arithmetic

Factoring is often the key to many shortcuts in arithmetic and in the rules used in quick mental computation. Have you heard of the "trick" to be used in multiplying any two-digit number by 11? The answer is immediately obtained by writing down the two digits with a space between them in which you write their sum. For example, $11 \cdot 45 = 4\ 9\ 5$. Here we wrote the 4 and 5 far enough apart to write their sum between them. Another way of saying this is to write the left digit in the hundreds column, the right digit in the units column and the sum of the digits in the tens column. Of course when the sum of the digits is greater than 9, you must increase the hundreds digit by one, for example, $11 \cdot 75 = 8\ 2\ 5$. You can convince yourself that this "makes sense" by solving enough of the problems in the usual way. But let us examine this trick or "rule" more closely.

Let the problem be $11 \cdot ab$, where a and b represent digits. Now $11 \cdot ab = (10 + 1)(a \cdot 10 + b)$. Performing this multiplication we find $a \cdot 100 + (a \cdot 10 + b \cdot 10) + b$. Factoring out the 10 in the two middle terms, we obtain $a \cdot 100 + (a + b) \cdot 10 + b$. Upon examining this result, it becomes clear that the product of 11 and any two-digit number can be expressed by writing the first digit a in the hundreds column, the sum of the digits $a + b$ in the tens column, and the second digit b in the units column. In other words, between the digits, insert their sum.

This rule can be extended to multiplying any number of digits by eleven. For example, to multiply $234,543 \cdot 11$, we write $2,579,973$ immediately by writing the first digit followed by the sum of it and the second digit, followed by the sum of the second and the third digits, etc.

Do you know how some people can square any number ending in

5 quickly? Let us develop a rule so we too can do this mentally. Our problem is to multiply out the number $(10a + 5)(10a + 5)$, where a is an element of C. For example, if $a = 3$, the problem is to find the square of 35.

$$(10 \cdot 3 + 5)(10 \cdot 3 + 5) = 35 \cdot 35 = (35)^2$$

Multiplying the expanded form of the general case, we obtain

$(10a \cdot 10a) + (5 \cdot 10a + 10a \cdot 5) + 5 \cdot 5$
  $a^2 \cdot 100 + (a \cdot 50 + a \cdot 50) + 25$ (commuting and multiplying)
  $a^2 \cdot 100 + a(50 + 50) + 25$ (factoring the middle term)
  $a^2 \cdot 100 + a \cdot 100 + 25$ (adding)
$(a^2 + a)100 + 25$ (factoring the first term)
$a(a + 1)100 + 25$ (factoring again)

This last expression is a handy solution form for the problem of finding the square of any number ending in 5.

Translating this solution form into words, we form a "rule" for finding the square of a multiple of 5: "write the product of the tens digit and the next greater digit and write 25 after it." Let us apply this rule to 35^2. The product of 3 and 4 is 12, and writing 25 after 12 we find 1225 to be the answer.

Write the square of 45. Since $4 \cdot 5 = 20$, we can write down 2025. Does it check? To find the square of 75 we multiply $7 \cdot 8 = 56$, and we write down 5625 as the solution. Of course, with larger numbers, squaring becomes more difficult to do mentally. To find the square of 135, for example, we need to compute $13 \cdot 14$ to find their product 182. But when we have done this, we can write down 18,225 as the answer.

Most such rules for quick computation can be verified or *invented* by the application of the algebraic principles reviewed so far. After you verify such a rule yourself, it becomes a logical rule rather than a trick.

**EXERCISES
3.6**

Write the product immediately for each of the following.

1.	$11 \cdot 81$	5.	$11 \cdot 26$	9.	$11 \cdot 65$
2.	$11 \cdot 23$	6.	$11 \cdot 53$	10.	$11 \cdot 55$
3.	$11 \cdot 45$	7.	$11 \cdot 87$	11.	$11 \cdot 243$
4.	$11 \cdot 34$	8.	$11 \cdot 49$	12.	$11 \cdot 451$

Write the square immediately.

13. 35^2 16. 95^2

14. 75^2 17. 115^2

15. 55^2 18. 105^2

19. Find the sum of the following ten numbers:

2, 3, 5, 8, 13, 21, 34, 55, 89, 144

    a. We can find the sum asked for above by multiplying the seventh number by 11 ($11 \cdot 34 = 374$). We can even state as a "rule" that the sum of the numbers in any series of this type can be found by multiplying the seventh number by 11. The series must have ten numbers, and the numbers are determined by selecting any two counting numbers as the first two numbers; the third number is the sum of the first two; the fourth number is the sum of the second and third numbers; the fifth number is the sum of the third and fourth, etc. Check this "rule" by finding the sum of the series beginning with the numbers 1 and 4.

    b. Check the "rule" in part a for the general case. That is, begin with x and y for the first two numbers.

3.7 Special Factors

Since we can capitalize on the zero property only when we can find factors whose product is zero, factoring skills need to be acquired. Many easily factored polynomials appear to be difficult until you recognize the special forms of the factors. Only three such particular factors will be discussed here. These should suffice to reinforce the concept and establish the mechanical skill you will need to follow the discussion.

Special Factor I

$$x^2 - b^2 = (x + b)(x - b)$$

    The difference of two squares factors into the product of the sum and the difference of the base numbers. Verify this by multiplying several binomials that are the sum and the difference of two terms. Note carefully the following equations; each was written by recognizing the left-hand side to be the difference of two squares.

1. $x^2 - 36 = (x + 6)(x - 6)$

2. $1 - x^2 = (1 + x)(1 - x)$

3. $a^2x^2 - b^2 = (ax + b)(ax - b)$

4. $25a^2 - 4b^2 = (5a + 2b)(5a - 2b)$

It is often helpful to write an intermediate step to better identify the squared terms.

5. $16x^2 - 9y^6 \quad = (4x)^2 - (3y^3)^2 = (4x + 3y^3)(4x - 3y^3)$

6. $36a^4 - 49b^{12} = (6a^2)^2 - (7b^6)^2 = (6a^2 + 7b^6)(6a^2 - 7b^6)$

Often, the extraction of a common factor leaves the difference of two squares.

7. $32x^2 - 18y^2 = 2(16x^2 - 9y^2) = 2(4x + 3y)(4x - 3y)$

8. $12m^5 - 27mn^8 = 3m(4m^4 - 9n^8)$
$$= 3m[(2m^2)^2 - (3n^4)^2] = 3m(2m^2 + 3n^4)(2m^2 - 3n^4)$$

Special Factor II

$$a^2 + 2ab + b^2 = (a + b)(a + b) = (a + b)^2$$

or

$$a^2 - 2ab + b^2 = (a - b)(a - b) = (a - b)^2$$

If the first and last terms of a trinomial are squares, and the middle term is twice the product of the square roots of the first and last terms, then the trinomial can be written as the square of the sum of the square roots of the first and last terms. For example,

1. $x^2 + 4x + 4 = (x + 2)^2$

2. $4x^2 + 4xy + y^2 = (2x)^2 + 4xy + y^2 = (2x + y)^2$

3. $m^2 - 2m + 1 = (m - 1)^2$

4. $x^2 - 6xy + 9y^2 = (x - 3y)^2$

5. $49a^4 + 28a^2b^2 + 4b^4 = (7a^2)^2 + 2(14a^2b^2) + (2b^2)^2 = (7a^2 + 2b^2)^2$

6. $x^2y^6 - 2xy^3z^4 + z^8 = (xy^3)^2 - 2xy^3z^4 + (z^4)^2 = (xy^3 - z^4)^2$

7. $(x + y)^2 + 2(x + y) + 1 = (x + y + 1)^2$

Verify the above by multiplying the given factors to make sure the polynomial on the left-hand side is obtained. In some of the older, standard algebra texts (where rules were particularly appreciated) the rule for extracting the square root of a perfect trinomial square was stated as: "extract the square roots of the first and last terms and connect these square roots by the sign of the middle term."

Did you ever learn how to find the square root of a counting number? If you once did, it would not be unusual if you were not able to recall the algorithm you used. Assuming that you cannot find the square root of such a number as 1156, except by trial and error methods, do you see anything in special factor II that might indicate to you how you could proceed to find the square root in a logical manner?

Since we know that 100 squared is 10,000 and 10 squared is 100, the square root of 1156 obviously must be a two-digit number. A two-digit number can be written as $t + u$, where t represents the number of tens and u represents the number of units. Now this number squared can be written according to special factor II as $(t + u)^2 = t^2 + 2tu + u^2$. With this beginning, try to develop a system for finding square roots.

CHECK YOUR WORK on page 115

As a real challenge, you may want to try developing a method for finding the cube root of a number. For example, it is both interesting and fun to note that for any perfect cube a^3 ($a \in Ra$), the cube root can be found through prime factorization of a^3.

For example, let us find the cube root of 13,824. We find the prime factors as follows:

$$
\begin{array}{ll}
432 & 3 \\
2)\overline{864} & 3)\overline{9} \\
2)\overline{1728} & 3)\overline{27} \\
2)\overline{3456} & 2)\overline{54} \\
2)\overline{6912} & 2)\overline{108} \\
2)\overline{13824} & 2)\overline{216} \\
& 2)\overline{432}
\end{array}
$$

$$13{,}824 = 2 \cdot 2 \cdot 2 \cdot 2 \cdot 2 \cdot 2 \cdot 2 \cdot 2 \cdot 2 \cdot 3 \cdot 3 \cdot 3$$
$$= (2 \cdot 2 \cdot 2 \cdot 3)(2 \cdot 2 \cdot 2 \cdot 3)(2 \cdot 2 \cdot 2 \cdot 3)$$
$$13{,}824 = (2^3 \cdot 3)^3 = (8 \cdot 3)^3 = 24^3$$

so

$$\sqrt[3]{13{,}824} = 24$$

Similarly, we find $\sqrt[3]{1.728}$ by

$$
\begin{array}{r}
0.003 \\
3\overline{)\,0.009} \\
3\overline{)\,0.027} \\
2\overline{)\,0.054} \\
2\overline{)\,0.108} \\
2\overline{)\,0.216} \\
2\overline{)\,0.432} \\
2\overline{)\,0.864} \\
2\overline{)\,1.728}
\end{array}
$$

$$1.728 = 2^3 \cdot 2^3 \cdot (0.003 \cdot 3 \cdot 3) = 2^3 \cdot 2^3 \cdot (0.3)^3 = (2 \cdot 2 \cdot 0.3)^3$$
$$= (4 \cdot 0.3)^3 = 1.2^3$$

and

$$\sqrt[3]{1.728} = 1.2$$

Find the prime factors of a few more cube roots yourself and see why this method will always work. Can you now develop a set of rules for an algorithm to find the cube root of *any* element of *Ra*?

Special Factor III

$$xy + ay + bx + ab = (x + a)(y + b)$$

Sometimes terms can be grouped to show a common *compound* factor. In the above case, if we first associate $(xy + ay) + (bx + ab)$ and then use the distributive property to factor out the y in the first term and the b in the second, we obtain $y(x + a) + b(x + a)$. It is clear now that each term has the common factor of $(x + a)$. Factoring out the common factor, we find $(x + a)(y + b)$.

Check the following (one of them is incorrect—which one?):

1. $ac + ad + bc + bd = (a + b)(c + d)$

2. $x^2 + xy + xz + yz = (x + z)(x + y)$

3. $25 - 5y + 5a - ay = 5(5 - y) + a(5 - y) = (5 - y)(5 + a)$

4. $3b - 7a - ab + 21 = (3 - a)(7 - b)$

5. $2x^2 - 6xy - xz + 3yz = (2x - z)(x - 3y)$

In problem 3 above we first resolved the four terms into two terms by factoring the first two terms into 5 and $(5 - y)$ and by factoring out the common factor of a in the last two terms. This clearly showed that the two newly formed terms had a common factor of $(5 - y)$.

Did you find the error in problem 4? The correct factors are $(3 - a)$ and $(7 + b)$. In factoring this sort of polynomial, many students have difficulty when faced with a result of the following form:

$$c(a - b) + d(b - a)$$

On inspection, we can see that the second factor in both terms contains the elements a and b, but with different signs. To resolve this problem we need only view the second term as $d(-1 \cdot -1 \cdot b + -1 \cdot a)$. Extracting the common factor of -1, we obtain $-d(-1b + a)$. Commuting, we see that $-d(a - b)$ has the factor $(a - b)$ in common with the first term given above. Another way of viewing this is to mentally multiply the second term twice by -1, which, in effect, is the same as multiplying by the multiplicative identity $+1$. Thus $-1d \cdot -1(b - a)$ equals $-1d(-1b + a)$ or $-d(a - b)$.

Let us ask ourselves again—why are we examining and reviewing factoring? We can best answer this question if we return to the area problems of the Greeks. Do you recall the time necessary to solve the area problems on page 79? Let us solve the first one now by factoring.

$$x^2 + 10x = 39$$

Subtracting 39 from both sides of the equation we first obtain a quadratic set equal to zero, $x^2 + 10x - 39 = 0$. Seeing no common factor among the three terms and failing to recognize any of the special factors here, we proceed to factor by the process of "reasoned inspection." We know that if the quadratic has integral solutions, it can be factored and takes the form of $(x +)(x -)$. We know the signs must differ, so that the product of the two second terms is negative. Listing the pairs whose product is 39, we find $(1, 39)$ and $(3, 13)$. The latter pair differ by 10; since their sum must be a positive 10, we assign the negative sign to the 3 and obtain the factors $(x + 13)(x - 3)$. Setting each of these equal to zero, we find that the roots are -13 and 3.

Factoring permits us to solve otherwise very difficult or tedious problems. Algebra provides us with a time-saving tool and is itself an ingenious process unifying much of the structure of mathematics.

As a final example, suppose you needed to build two square areas totaling 340 square feet. Because you can greatly reduce your costs, you decide to use lumber in exact foot lengths. You also decide to build one area with a side exactly 2 feet longer than the other. Find the length of the side of each square.

If the smaller side is x feet long, the larger square will have a side $x + 2$ feet long. The sum of the two areas will then be $x^2 + (x + 2)^2$ and must equal 340 square feet. Simplifying the equation,

$$x^2 + (x + 2)^2 = 340$$

we have

$x^2 + (x^2 + 4x + 4) = 340$	(squaring the binomial $(x + 2)$)
$(x^2 + x^2) + 4x + 4 = 340$	(associative property of addition)
$2x^2 + 4x + 4 - 340 = 0$	
$2x^2 + 4x - 336 = 0$	
$x^2 + 2x - 168 = 0$	(dividing through by 2)
$(x + 14)(x - 12) = 0$	(factoring)
$x = -14$ or $x = 12$	(using the zero property)

Since we are seeking a positive length, we reject the negative solution and check the positive solution as the length of the side of the smaller square. The side of the larger square is $x + 2$, or 14; so $12^2 + 14^2$ should equal 340 and it does, $144 + 196 = 340$.

Had the problem been stated in terms of numbers as, for example: "find two consecutive even digits such that the sum of their squares equals 340," we would not have discarded the negative answer, since -14 is a member of the set of integers. But then -14 is the smaller number and $-14 + 2 = -12$, which is the larger number. Checking this solution, we see that $(-14)^2 + (-12)^2$ also equals 340.

EXERCISES
3.7

Factor the following expressions.

1. $ay + by$
2. $2x + 4y$
3. $3x^2 - 6x$
4. $x^2 + y^2$
5. $4x^2 - 25$
6. $x^2 + 2xy + y^2$
7. $9c^2 + a^2 - 6ac$
8. $2x + 6 - 3y - xy$
9. $42 - xy + 3y - 14x$
10. $(a + b)^2 - c^2$
11. $3a^2x + a^2y - b^2y - 3b^2x$
12. $x^2 + 2xy + y^2 - 16z^2$
13. $x^4 + 9y^6 - 6x^2y^3 - 100$
14. $a^2 + 2ab + b^2 - c^2 - 2c - 1$

Solve for x in the following equations.

15. $2x + 12 = 2x^2$
16. $\frac{4}{9}x^2 - 16 = 0$
17. $2x^2 + 6 = 7x$

18. $2x^2 + 32 = 16x$
19. $x^2 + 2x = xy + 2y$
20. $(x - y)^2 = 1$

3.8 Completing the Square

So far we have limited our work to *polynomials over the set of integers;* that is, polynomials in which all of the constants are integers. Can you find the one exception in Exercises 3.7? Why were we able to solve this quadratic equation even though the coefficient of x^2 is a fraction rather than an integer?

All of our special factors were readily recognizable, and our procedure of reasoned inspection was facilitated because we limited our work to quadratic equations over the set of integers. Let us look at the problem again when we admit rationals as coefficients. Suppose we wish to solve the equation

$\frac{1}{3}x^2 + \frac{3}{4}x = 57$

We can always multiply the equation by the least common multiple of the denominators and thereby obtain a quadratic over the set of integers once more. Let us do so in this case. Multiplying through by 12, we obtain

$4x^2 + 9x = 684$

Now adding the additive inverse of 684 to each side:

$4x^2 + 9x - 684 = 0$

We have obtained the form of the equation most helpful to us if we are to factor the left side with what we know thus far. Few people are able to factor this expression quickly, even when told that it factors into two linear binomials in standard form over the set of integers. If you want to increase your self-confidence, find by inspection factors for

$\frac{2}{3}x^2 + \frac{3}{4}x = \frac{33}{4}$

Since we have shown that the factoring method is limited and often tedious *we must find another method of solving such quadratics.*

Let us consider the equation $x^2 - 6x = 7$. On examination of the left-hand side of this equation, we note that it contains the first two members of a trinomial with the characteristics of a perfect square as described for the special factor II on page 90. From $x^2 - 6x +$, we see that our third term must be one-half of 6 (or 3) squared if we are to make this trinomial a perfect square. Thus, if we write $x^2 - 6x + 3^2$ we have a trinomial that is the perfect square of $(x - 3)$. How does this help us?

Adding 3^2 to both sides of the original problem, we have

$$x^2 - 6x + 3^2 = 7 + 3^2$$

or simplifying,

$$(x - 3)^2 = 16$$
$$x - 3 = \pm 4$$

(Can you explain the use of both signs?)

$$x = 7 \quad \text{or} \quad x = -1$$

We have just solved an equation by a process called "completing the square." Since this sounds like what the Greeks were doing, let us take another look to see how the two procedures are related.

First, refer to Figure 3-8 on page 80, which illustrates the solution of the quadratic equation $x^2 + 10x = 39$ by following the thinking of the Greeks. To "complete the big square," an added area of 25 or 5^2 is shown. Solving this equation, using our new procedures, we first seek a number b such that $x^2 + 10x + b^2$ is a perfect square. Since one-half of 10 is 5 and the coefficient of the first term is 1, our third term must be 5^2. Adding this to both sides and solving within the universe of nonnegative numbers, we find

$$x^2 + 10x + 5^2 = 39 + 5^2$$
$$(x + 5)^2 = 39 + 25$$
$$(x + 5)^2 = 64 = 8^2$$
$$x + 5 = 8$$
$$x = 3$$

This is the answer we obtained and verified previously. Now the similarities between what we call "completing the square" and what the Greeks did in completing the square become clear. Notice in Figure 3-8 that the area needed to complete the square was found to be 5 by 5 or 5^2. We then added this area to the shaded area of 39 to find the total area of 64. But the side of the big square was $x + 5$ in length, so $(x + 5)^2$ had to be equal to the area of 64; therefore, $x + 5$ had to equal 8, or $x = 3$. This is exactly what we did above except that we did it from the knowledge that a trinomial of the form $x^2 + 2bx + b^2$ is a perfect square of the linear binomial $x + b$.

To clarify further the relationship between the two methods of "completing the square," let us solve another problem where the variable itself is a fraction. Given $4x^2 + 36x = 19$, we search for a third term such that $(2x)^2 + 36x + (\ \ )$ is a perfect square. Since two times the product of the coefficients of the first and third terms must equal 36, we know the coefficient of x in the factored form times our new number must equal 18; hence the number is 9, and we write

$$(2x)^2 + 36x + (9)^2 = 19 + (9)^2$$
$$(2x + 9)^2 = 19 + 81$$
$$(2x + 9)^2 = 100$$
$$2x + 9 = 10$$

Solving for x

$$2x = 10 - 9 = 1$$
$$x = \tfrac{1}{2}$$

(Since we are comparing this method to the Greek method, we are temporarily confining our work to the universe of nonnegative numbers.) If we solve this problem by the Greek method, we first draw a square of sides $2x$ and two rectangles of sides 9 and $2x$ as illustrated by the shaded area of Figure 3-10. We find from the drawing that the area necessary to complete the large square is a square 9 units by

Figure 3-10

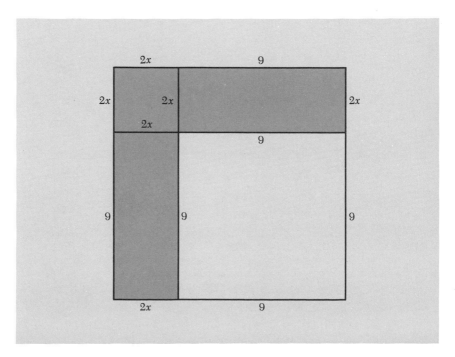

9 units or 81 square units. Adding 81 square units to the shaded area, we know that the total area of the large square is $19 + 81 = 100$ square units, and that each side must then be 10 units. Since the side of the large square is $2x + 9$, we obtain $2x + 9 = 10$. Solving for x as we did previously, we again find $x = \frac{1}{2}$.

Notice that in both procedures we have followed almost exactly the same steps. Indeed, the two procedures are just different ways of thinking out what the third term must be to complete the square.

Consider again the equation

$$\tfrac{1}{3}x^2 + \tfrac{3}{4}x = 57$$

If we first multiply through by 3 to obtain a perfect square in the first term, we obtain

$$x^2 + \tfrac{9}{4}x = 171$$

We draw the square in Figure 3-11 by first drawing the small square of side x and two equal rectangles of sides $\frac{9}{8}$ and x. $\frac{9}{8}$ is exactly one-half of $\frac{9}{4}$, so the total area of these two rectangles is $\frac{9}{4}x$. The area needed to complete the large square is seen to be $(\frac{9}{8})^2$. Using the algebraic method of finding this number, we note that to complete the square on the left-hand side of $x^2 + \frac{9}{4}x = 171$, we need to add a perfect

Figure 3-11

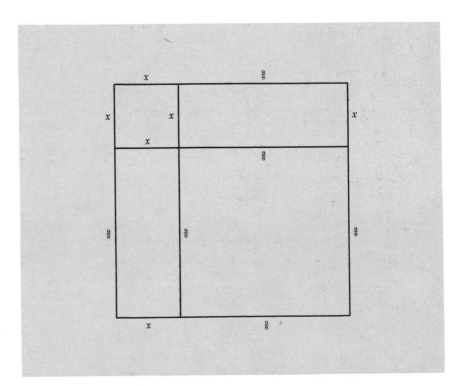

square, the square root of which is exactly one-half the coefficient of the middle term. Since $\frac{1}{2} \cdot \frac{9}{4} = \frac{9}{8}$, we know the number necessary to complete the square is $(\frac{9}{8})^2$, the same number obtained by the drawing method. Again we see that the two methods are simply different ways of *thinking* out the problem.

Solving the problem from this point is identical in either procedure.

$$x^2 + \frac{9}{4}x + \left(\frac{9}{8}\right)^2 = 171 + \left(\frac{9}{8}\right)^2$$

$$\left(x + \frac{9}{8}\right)^2 = 171 + \frac{81}{64} = \frac{10{,}944 + 81}{64} = \frac{11{,}025}{64}$$

$$\left(x + \frac{9}{8}\right)^2 = \left(\frac{105}{8}\right)^2$$

$$x + \frac{9}{8} = \frac{105}{8} \qquad \text{or} \qquad 8x + 9 = 105$$

$$8x = 96 \qquad \text{and} \qquad x = 12$$

You should now be able to find the other factor, since you know one already. That is, $x^2 + \frac{9}{4}x - 171 = (x - 12)(x + ?) = 0$.

See how well you can do using both methods, the drawing and the algebraic, to solve

$$\tfrac{2}{3}x^2 + \tfrac{3}{4}x = \tfrac{33}{4}$$

CHECK YOUR WORK on page 116

We have not yet attempted solutions to quadratic equations over the set of real numbers. Consider the equation

$$\tfrac{1}{2}x^2 - \sqrt{2}x - \sqrt{3} = 0$$

If we first multiply through by 2 and then solve by completing the square we find one real root

$$x = \sqrt{2} + \sqrt{2 + 2\sqrt{3}}$$

Obtain this answer on your own and verify it by direct substitution in the given equation.

EXERCISES
3.8

Find the solution set in R for the following by using the method of completing the square:

1. $x^2 - 2x = 8$
2. $x^2 - 2x = 3$
3. $x^2 - 8x = 65$
4. $x^2 + 6x = 27$
5. $x^2 + 5x = 14$
6. $2x^2 + x = 15$
7. $2x^2 - 17x = 9$
8. $6x^2 + x = 1$
9. $18x^2 + 9x = 2$
10. $12x^2 + 2 = 11x$
11. $15x^2 = 1 + 2x$
12. $5x^2 + 3x = 2$

3.9 The Quadratic Formula

Is it possible to develop a *general* formula for solving such quadratic equations over the real numbers? Let us write the general quadratic equation and pursue a solution.

$$ax^2 + bx + c = 0$$

where all three coefficients are elements of R and $a \neq 0$. Once more we are seeking a generalized solution to a particular kind of problem because we are not fully satisfied with the solution procedures we have used to solve *specific* problems. As in the preceding problems, let us complete the square using both approaches.

First, we divide through by the coefficient of x and obtain the equivalent equation

$$x^2 + \frac{b}{a}x + \frac{c}{a} = 0$$

Adding the additive inverse of c/a to both sides, we obtain

$$x^2 + \frac{b}{a}x = -\frac{c}{a}$$

From Figure 3-12, it is clear the third term necessary to complete the square is

$$\left(\frac{b}{2a}\right)^2$$

Now let us use the second approach. We have learned that when the coefficient of x^2 is 1, the third term is the square of one-half of the coefficient of the second term. Therefore we obtain $(b/2a)^2$. Adding this to both sides, we have

$$x^2 + \frac{b}{a}x + \left(\frac{b}{2a}\right)^2 = \left(\frac{b}{2a}\right)^2 - \frac{c}{a}$$

$$\left(x + \frac{b}{2a}\right)^2 = \frac{b^2}{4a^2} - \frac{c}{a}$$

$$\left(x + \frac{b}{2a}\right)^2 = \frac{b^2 - 4ac}{4a^2}$$ (by obtaining a common denominator for the right-hand side)

$$x + \frac{b}{2a} = \frac{\pm\sqrt{b^2 - 4ac}}{2a}$$ (taking the square root of both sides)

$$x - \frac{-b}{2a} \pm \frac{\sqrt{b^2 - 4ac}}{2a}$$ (adding the additive inverse of $b/2a$ to both sides)

$$x = \frac{-b + \sqrt{b^2 - 4ac}}{2a} \quad \text{or} \quad x = \frac{-b - \sqrt{b^2 - 4ac}}{2a}$$

We have found a formula for finding the real roots of any quadratic equation in one variable. As you should remember, this formula is called the *quadratic formula*. By substituting the coefficients of the three terms of a quadratic equation in the quadratic formula, the real roots can be found.

Let us use the quadratic formula to solve a quadratic equation we could easily solve by factoring. Consider $x^2 - 7x + 12 = 0$. In this

Figure 3-12

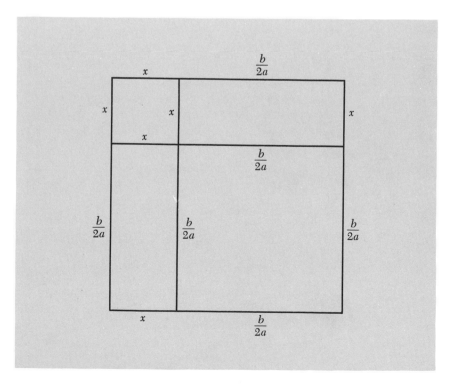

case, $a = 1$, $b = -7$, and $c = 12$. Substituting into the quadratic formula, we have

$$x = \frac{-(-7) \pm \sqrt{(-7)^2 - (4 \cdot 1 \cdot 12)}}{2 \cdot 1}$$

$$x = \frac{7 \pm \sqrt{49 - 48}}{2} = \frac{7 \pm \sqrt{1}}{2} = \frac{7 \pm 1}{2}$$

$$x = \frac{8}{2} \qquad x = \frac{6}{2}$$

$$x = 4 \qquad \text{or} \qquad x = 3$$

The solutions are 4 and 3. The factors are $(x - 4)$ and $(x - 3)$.

Now, use the formula on the following, more difficult, problem, which you have already solved by completing the square.

$$\tfrac{2}{3}x^2 + \tfrac{3}{4}x - \tfrac{33}{4} = 0$$

$$x = \frac{-\tfrac{3}{4} \pm \sqrt{(\tfrac{3}{4})^2 - 4 \cdot \tfrac{2}{3} \cdot (-\tfrac{33}{4})}}{2 \cdot \tfrac{2}{3}} = \frac{-\tfrac{3}{4} \pm \sqrt{\tfrac{9}{16} + 22}}{\tfrac{4}{3}}$$

$$= \frac{-\tfrac{3}{4} \pm \sqrt{\tfrac{9}{16} + \tfrac{352}{16}}}{\tfrac{4}{3}} = \frac{-\tfrac{3}{4} \pm \sqrt{\tfrac{361}{16}}}{\tfrac{4}{3}} = \frac{-\tfrac{3}{4} \pm \tfrac{19}{4}}{\tfrac{4}{3}}$$

$$x = \frac{-\tfrac{3}{4} + \tfrac{19}{4}}{\tfrac{4}{3}} \qquad x = \frac{-\tfrac{3}{4} - \tfrac{19}{4}}{\tfrac{4}{3}}$$

$$x = \tfrac{16}{4} \div \tfrac{4}{3} = 4 \cdot \tfrac{3}{4} = 3$$

or

$$x = -\tfrac{22}{4} \div \tfrac{4}{3} = -\tfrac{22}{4} \cdot \tfrac{3}{4} = -\tfrac{33}{8}$$

Thus the solutions are 3 and $-\tfrac{33}{8}$. The factors are $(x - 3)$ and $(x + \tfrac{33}{8})$. Multiplying the factors, we find $x^2 + \tfrac{9}{8}x - \tfrac{99}{8}$, the form of the equation we found after multiplying through by the reciprocal of the coefficient of x^2.

Notice that in each problem we have solved so far, we have successfully found answers that were elements of the set of real numbers. The reason for this is that we have carefully chosen the problems so that we might complete the development of the quadratic formula without being side-tracked. This has been accomplished, and we must now look at a major limitation of the quadratic formula.

Do you recall from Figure 3-4 (see page 75) the two equations whose graphs apparently had no real roots? They were

$$x^2 + 4 = y \tag{2}$$

$$x^2 - 4x + 8 = y \tag{9}$$

Neither graph intersected the x axis. That is, when $y = 0$, there is apparently no real number solution for x. Let us apply the quadratic formula to equation (2), when $y = 0$.

$$x = \frac{-0 \pm \sqrt{0 - 4 \cdot 1 \cdot 4}}{2 \cdot 1} = \frac{\pm \sqrt{-16}}{2}$$

But what is the square root of -16? What is the square root of any negative number? Since the square of any real number is a positive real number, the square root of a negative number is meaningless in the universe of real numbers. We say this quadratic has no real roots, and this is confirmed by its graph.

Try solving equation (9) when $y = 0$. Again you find you are faced with finding the square root of a negative number. In a sense, we have failed to obtain closure. Just as we lacked closure under sub-traction in the set of counting numbers, we might say we lack closure under the operation of finding the square root within the set of real numbers. Just as we were motivated to expand the set of counting numbers to find an answer to $5 - 8 = ?$, we are now motivated to expand the set R to find the answer to $\sqrt{-16}/2 = ?$ Before we under-take this expansion, however, we have other things to do, including a final look at the quadratic formula.

Students tend to commit the quadratic formula to memory during most algebra courses, only to find that a year later it is no longer subject to recall. To be sure, it is handy to have this formula memo-rized during periods of frequent need (for instance, during a course), but how much better and more permanent the knowledge of the formula would be if the ideas of "where it came from," "what it means," and "what it is used for" were really grasped to begin with.

As you use the quadratic formula, try not to lose sight of the answers to the following questions:

1. *From where did it come?*   The quadratic formula came from solving the general quadratic equation $ax^2 + bx + c = 0$, x being a variable, a, b, $c \in R$, and $a \neq 0$. We call this deriving the formula. We did it by completing the square either through a drawing or by applying special factor II. It is the culmination of a brilliant process begun by the Greeks.

2. *What does it mean?*   The quadratic formula means we can find the real roots of any quadratic equation over the real num-bers. By arranging a quadratic equation in the standard form of $ax^2 + bx + c = 0$, direct substitution of the values of the coeffi-cients in the formula yield the real roots. Hence, any quadratic with real roots can be factored.

3. *What is it used for?* The quadratic formula is a powerful tool in dealing with algebraic expressions of the second degree. Using it, we can factor quadratic polynomials and find solution sets for these quadratic equations.

EXERCISES
3.9

Factor the following quadratics first by completing the square, second by the Greek method, and third, by using the quadratic formula.

1. $x^2 + 7x - 60$ 　　　　　　　2. $x^2 + \frac{1}{2}x - 3$

Solve the following for x by using the quadratic formula.

3. $x^2 + 24x + 80 = 0$ 　　　　9. $x^2 - 3x + 1 = 0$
4. $x^2 + x - 1 = 0$ 　　　　　10. $-3x^2 - 2x + 1 = 0$
5. $4x^2 - 12x + 9 = 0$ 　　　　11. $x^2 - 2x + \frac{1}{2} = 0$
6. $3x^2 - 2x - \frac{1}{4} = 0$ 　　　　12. $\frac{1}{3}x^2 + \frac{1}{2} - 1 = 0$
7. $3x^2 + 8x + \frac{7}{3} = 0$ 　　　　13. $-\frac{1}{2}x^2 + 5x - 8 = 0$
8. $-2x^2 + 3x + 1 = 0$

SUMMARY ───────────────────────────

In this chapter we found that quadratics can be graphed on a system of Cartesian coordinates. Much can be predicted about a graph from its equation and conversely much can be told about the equation from the graph.

The Greek approach to completing the square of a quadratic equation to find a nonnegative solution was thoroughly developed.

The laws of exponents were reviewed and summarized for the real numbers raised to integral powers.

The factoring of quadratics established the advantage of following these general procedures:

1. Extract all common factors.

2. Inspect for special factors such as the difference of two squares.

3. If possible, factor by reasoned inspection, using your knowledge of the general product of two binomials.

4. Use the quadratic formula.

The vocabulary used in working with polynomials was reviewed and terms such as monomial, binomial, polynomial, and degree of an equation were defined.

We have examined the relationships between the different approaches to solving a quadratic equation. The similarities between the Greek and algebraic methods of completing the square were especially examined. Both of these led to the quadratic formula—the ultimate solution of the general equation, which has the form $ax^2 + bx + c = 0$.

Because of the space allocated to reviewing and examining procedures and skills, it was often difficult to maintain a view of the structure of mathematics and to note the interdependence of all the ideas and procedures. We examined the idea that algebra is a generalized extension of the real numbers, completely integrated and dependent therein, and yet furnishing us greater power and speed in using the real numbers.

Taking the square root of negative numbers was carefully avoided in both discussion and in exercises, since the operation is never possible when $U = R$. That is, the set of real numbers is not closed under this operation. We admitted the need for such closure, but delayed discussion and the extension of the number system until a later chapter when the need will be even more demanding.

To summarize the many methods we learned in this chapter, let us solve a problem in as many different ways as possible. In translating a hypothetical problem into an equation suppose we were to obtain

$$x^2 + 2x + (3y)^0 = y + 9$$

where y is in terms of dollars and cents and x is in terms of the number of items we manufacture and sell each day. Our desire is to make a profit so that we may stay in business. It would be important, therefore, to know how many items we must sell each day so as not to *lose* money. That is, what value must x have if y is to be zero or greater?

Recalling that any nonzero number raised to the zero power is equal to 1, we write the equation as

$$x^2 + 2x + 1 = y + 9$$

Adding the additive inverse of 9 to each side, we obtain

$$x^2 + 2x + 1 - 9 = y$$

Since we are interested in the special case, when $y = 0$, we have obtained a quadratic equation in standard form, $x^2 + 2x - 8 = 0$, which we solve in four different ways.

1. Graphing

Substituting the values of $0, -1, 2, -5, 4$, arbitrarily chosen for x, in $x^2 + 2x - 8 = y$, we complete the following table of values for y:

x	0	−1	2	−5	4
y	−8	−9	0	7	16

These ordered pairs are plotted in Figure 3-13. Recalling that the x intercepts are the solutions of the equation when $y = 0$, we have found one of the solutions in our table, $x = 2$. An intelligent guess, after examining Figure 3-13, would be that the other solution might be $x = -4$. To check this we find $(-4)^2 + 2(-4) - 8 = 16 - 8 - 8 = 0$. Therefore, the other solution is, indeed, −4. Since we are in the business of selling, we reject −4 as a solution, and know that we must sell at least two items to keep from losing money.

2. The Greek Solution

Viewing the equation as the Greeks did, we draw a square with side x and two rectangles, each with sides x and 1, as in Figure 3-14. The equation is put in the form $x^2 + 2x = 8$. The shaded areas of the figure are equal to 8, and the area added to complete the large square is 1 by 1, or 1. Thus the total area equals 9, making each side of the large square equal 3. But each side is $x + 1$. Setting this equal to 3, we find $x = 3 - 1 = 2$. Again, we must sell at least two items daily to keep from showing a loss.

3. Factoring

The equation in the form $x^2 + 2x - 8 = 0$ can be factored by reasoned inspection. We search for factors of the type $(x + \ )(x - \ )$. The product of our first terms gives us the necessary x^2. We know the

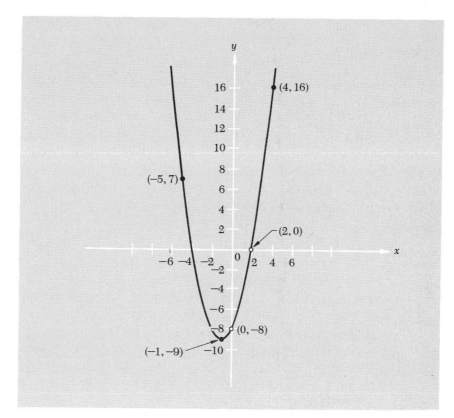

Figure 3-13

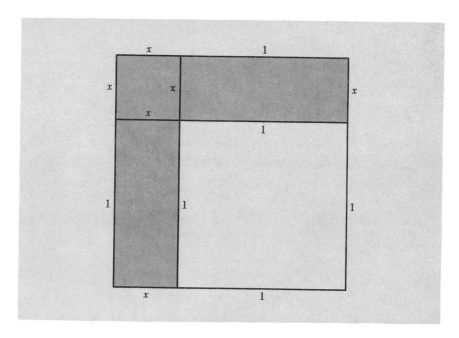

Figure 3-14

signs must differ, because the product of the second terms must be a negative 8. Listing the pairs of factors whose products are 8, we find $(1, 8)$ and $(2, 4)$. Since the middle term of the trinomial demands that the pair differ by 2, we select the pair $(2, 4)$ and assign the negative sign to the smaller of the two numbers. We multiply and obtain

$$(x + 4)(x - 2) = x^2 + 2x - 8 = 0$$

Having resolved the quadratic into factors, we set each factor equal to zero and find

$$x + 4 = 0 \qquad \text{or} \qquad x - 2 = 0$$
$$x = -4 \qquad \text{or} \qquad x = 2$$

4. Using the Quadratic Formula

Writing the equation in the general form, $x^2 + 2x - 8 = 0$, we substitute the coefficients in the appropriate positions of the quadratic formula and obtain

$$x = \frac{-2 \pm \sqrt{2^2 - 4 \cdot 1 \cdot (-8)}}{2 \cdot 1} = \frac{-2 \pm \sqrt{4 + 32}}{2}$$
$$= \frac{-2 \pm \sqrt{36}}{2} = \frac{-2 \pm 6}{2} = -1 \pm 3$$

The solutions are again $x = 2$ or $x = -4$.

CHAPTER REVIEW TEST

1. Calculate 18^2 and then subtract 12^2 from your result. Now work the same problem using your knowledge of special factors — $18^2 - 12^2 = (18 + 12)(18 - 12) = ?$ Compare the amount of work required by each method.

2. Repeat the procedure of problem 1 for $113^2 - 87^2 = ?$

3. Calculate $43^2 + 2 \cdot 43 \cdot 57 + 57^2 = ?$ by two methods.

4. Solve $4 \cdot 4^2 + 16 \cdot 12 + 4 \cdot 6^2 = ?$ by two methods.

5. Find the product of $(60 + 7)(80 - 3)$ by using the means and extremes rule. Verify your answer by multiplying $67 \cdot 77$.

6. Solve $(100 - 2)(100 + 8) = ?$ by the means and extremes rule.

7. Prove: $\sqrt{2} \div 3 \neq \sqrt{2} - 3$.

8. Prove: $\sqrt{a} \div b \neq \sqrt{a} - b$, where $a, b \in R, b \neq 0$, and $\sqrt{a} \in Irr$.

9. Using the fact that $(t + u)^2 = t^2 + 2tu + u^2$, determine logically the square root of 5184.

10. Find the square root of 17,424 using the technique developed in problem 9.

11. State why $3x^2 + 4x + 5$ is a quadratic.

12. Who was the greatest co-inventor in the field of mathematics?

13. Define "trinomial," and give an example of one.

14. $2x^7 + 4x^5 + x^2$ is a polynomial of what degree in x?

15. Graph a parabola and find its equation.

16. Explain how the means and extremes rule for multiplying two binomials is related to arithmetic in the elementary school.

17. Simplify the following expressions:

a. $\left(\dfrac{8x^2y^{-2}}{4xy^{-3}}\right)^3 \left(\dfrac{x^2y}{(2xy^2)^0}\right)^{-2}$

b. $\dfrac{(-2a^2b^2)^3}{2(ab^3)^2}$

18. Plot the graph of $x^2 + 2x + 1 = -y$.

19. Find the x intercepts for $y = 2x^2 - 13x - 7$.

20. Solve $x^2 + 12x - 28 = 0$ for x using the Greek method.

21. Factor: $y^2 - 4$; $3x^3 + 18x^2 + 15x$; $c^2y - 2a + 2c^2 - ay$.

22. Complete the square for $x^2 + 12x = 28$ and solve for x.

23. Solve $5x^2 - 7x = 6$ for x using the quadratic formula.

24. Explain the relationship between special factor II and finding the square root of a number.

25. Derive the quadratic formula.

26. Factoring is a sophisticated application of which property of the real number system. Explain.

27. What property of zero increases the importance of factoring? Explain why.

28. If y equals a second-degree polynomial in x, how many times does the graph of the equation intersect the y axis? the x axis?

29. Discuss the meaning of each of the three possible answers to the last question.

CHECKING YOUR WORK

page 74

The x intercepts are the solutions of the equations for $y = 0$. That is, they are the values of x when $y = 0$. When $y = 0$ in equation (3), we find that $x = +2$ or -2, and we write $x = \pm 2$. The solutions for equation (8) when $y = 0$ are seen from the graph to be $x = -4$ and $x = 2$. Substituting each of these in equation (8), we find for -4

$$(-4)^2 + 2(-4) - 8 = 16 - 8 - 8 = 0$$

Thus $x = -4$ is a solution. When $x = 2$, we find

$$2^2 + 2 \cdot 2 - 8 = 4 + 4 - 8 = 0$$

and 2 is also found to be a solution.

Return to page 74

page 81

2. $9x^2 + 6x = 48;$ $\qquad x = 2$

Check: $9(2)^2 + 6 \cdot 2 = 9 \cdot 4 + 12 = 36 + 12 = 48.$

For the shaded area we have (see Figure 3-15)

$$(3x)^2 + 1 \cdot 3x + 1 \cdot 3x = 9x^2 + 3x + 3x = 9x^2 + 6x = 48$$

The new area added is $1 \cdot 1 = 1$. The total area of new square is $48 + 1 = 49$. So each side equals 7. But a side equals $3x + 1$. So $3x + 1 = 7$; $3x = 6$; and $x = 2$.

3. $2x^2 + 4x = 70$

Since $2x^2$ is not a perfect square, we must make it so by multiplying the entire equation by 2. The result is $4x^2 + 8x = 140$, which can be solved like problem 2. The shaded area equals (see Figure 3-16)

$$(2x)^2 + 2 \cdot 2x + 2 \cdot 2x = 4x^2 + 4x + 4x = 4x^2 + 8x = 140$$

The new added area equals $2 \cdot 2 = 4$; therefore, the total area of the large square is $4 + 140 = 144$. Each side must equal 12. But each side is $2x + 2$, so $2x + 2 = 12$; $2x = 10$; and $x = 5$.

Check: $2(5)^2 + 4 \cdot 5 = 70$, $2 \cdot 25 + 20 = 70$, $50 + 20 = 70$.

Figure
3-15

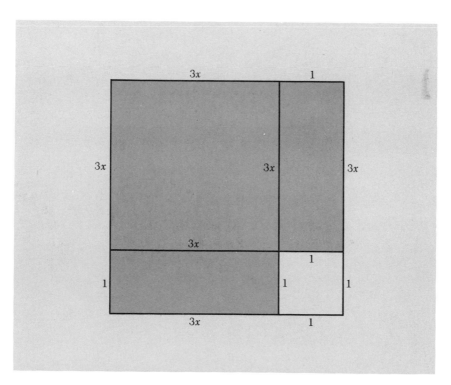

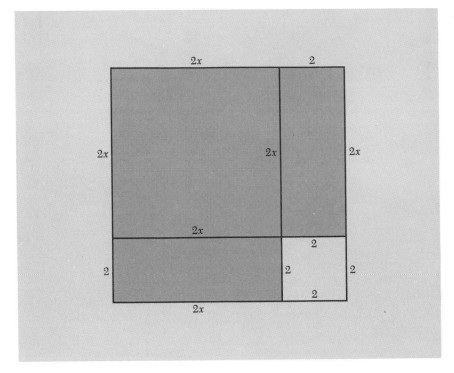

**Figure
3-16**

Would the problem be simpler if we first divided the equation by 2 rather than multiplying? Try it and see.

4. $x^2 - 4x = 12$

This problem is different in that the coefficient of x is negative. One way of proceeding is as follows. Draw a large square of area x^2 (see Figure 3-17). Subtract the two shaded rectangular portions of area $2 \cdot x$. Since these two rectangles have an area of intersection of $2 \cdot 2$, subtract this amount again, as shown in the dotted area to obtain a true representation of what is left of the original x^2. This area is equal to $(x - 2)^2 - (2 \cdot 2)$ or $(x - 2)^2 - 4 = 12$. Adding 4 to each side, we find

$$(x - 2)^2 = 12 + 4, \text{ or } (x - 2)^2 = 16$$

Taking the square root of each side, we find $(x - 2) = 4$. Thus, $x = 4 + 2 = 6$.

Check: $6^2 - 4 \cdot 6 = 36 - 24 = 12$.

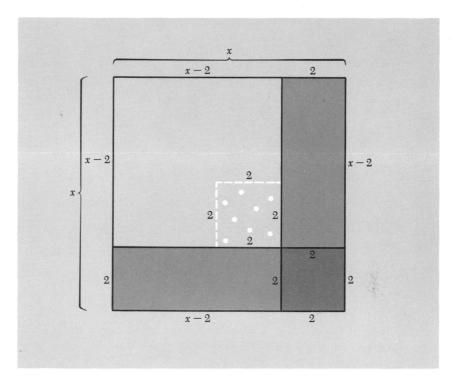

Figure
3-17

5. $x^2 + 3x = 4$

The difficulty here is that the coefficient of x is an odd number. We make it even by multiplying the equation by 2, $2x^2 + 6x = 8$. But now, as in problem 3, the coefficient of x^2 is not a perfect square, so we multiply again by 2 to obtain $4x^2 + 12x = 16$. We can now draw the figure and see that the added area necessary to complete the large square is 9 (see Figure 3-18). Therefore $(2x + 3)^2 = 9 + 16 = 25$ and $2x + 3 = 5$, so $2x = 5 - 3$, $x = 1$.

Check: $1^2 + 3 \cdot 1 = 1 + 3 = 4$.

6. $x^2 - 6x = 7$

From the large square of side x (see Figure 3-19), subtract the vertical rectangular area of $3 \cdot x$ and the horizontal rectangular area of $3 \cdot x$. Since these rectangles have an area of intersection of 9, the darker area, subtract this area once more to achieve the necessary subtraction of a full $6x$. Now the area remaining equals 7 and can be

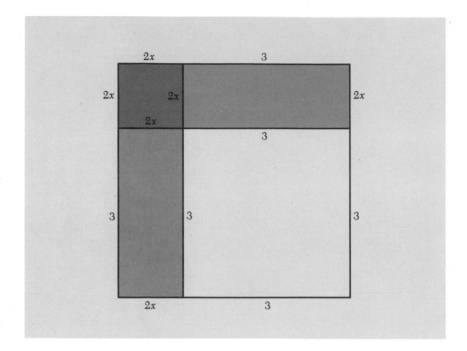

**Figure
3-18**

**Figure
3-19**

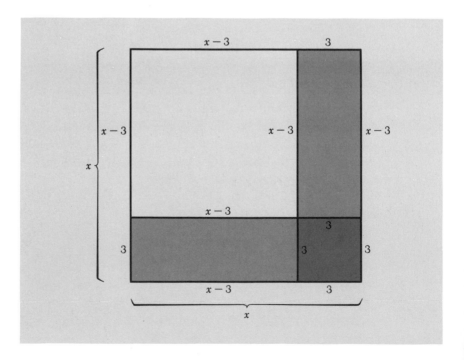

written as $(x-3)^2 = 9 + 7$, or $(x-3)^2 = 16$, so $x - 3 = 4$ and $x = 7$.
Check: $7^2 - 6 \cdot 7 = 49 - 42 = 7$.

Return to page 81

page 91 Given $(t + u)^2 = t^2 + 2tu + u^2 = 1156$, we must find the values of t and u. What is the largest multiple of 10, which, when squared, is equal to or less than 1156? We know that $20^2 = 400$; $40^2 = 1600$; and $30^2 = 900$, which is the value sought. But if $t = 30$, then what is $2tu$? It must be equal to or less than 256 because t^2 has already accounted for 900 of the original 1156. But if $2tu \leq 256$, then $2 \cdot 30u \leq 256$ and $60u \leq 256$. The largest value of u that satisfies the condition is $u = 4$. Having found t and u, we know that the square root of 1156 is 34. We can develop the following procedure.

$$1156 = (t + u)^2$$
$$1156 = t^2 + 2tu + u^2$$
$$\text{if } t = 30, \ t^2 = 900 \quad \text{and} \quad 2t = 60$$
$$1156 - 900 = 256 = 60u + u^2$$
$$\text{if } u = 4, \ 60 \cdot 4 = 240 \leq 256 \quad \text{and} \quad u^2 = 16$$
$$256 - 240 = \ 16 = 4^2$$

Check: $t^2 + 2tu + u^2 = 30^2 + 2 \cdot 30 \cdot 4 + 4^2 = 1156$

We can now see the origin of the common algorithm for finding square roots.

$$
\begin{array}{r}
\underline{34} \\
4 \\
3\ 0 \\
\overline{)\,1156} \\
9 \\
64\ \overline{)\,256} \\
256
\end{array}
$$

To find the square root by the above method use the following steps:

1. Point off with a caret every two digits to the left from the decimal point.

2. Write, above the digit just preceding the last caret to the left, the number which when squared will be the largest number that is equal to or less than the number immediately below it (t).

3. Subtract and bring down the next pair of digits (forming a dividend).

4. *Double* the present quotient, and write this number ($2t$) to the left of the new dividend. This number represents the number of tens that you will divide into the new dividend.

5. Find the unit digit of the new divisor in such a way that when multiplied times the number of tens plus itself, the product will be the greatest number that is equal to or less than the dividend.

6. If the original counting number was a perfect square, this process will yield the exact square root.

Thus algebra (and in particular, special factor II) again helped us to establish a way of finding answers that might otherwise have been found only through trial and error. The purpose of this little side trip was, again, an effort to show the power of the generalized equation in helping us determine a way to solve *any* problem of a particular kind rather than the limited arithmetical solution of a particular case.

Return to page 91

Return to page 91

**page
99**

It is always helpful to multiply through by the reciprocal of the coefficient of the first term. In this case, we multiply through by $\frac{3}{2}$.

$$\frac{3}{2}(\frac{2}{3}x^2 + \frac{3}{4}x) = \frac{3}{2} \cdot \frac{33}{4}$$

$$x^2 + \frac{9}{8}x = \frac{99}{8}$$

$$x^2 + \frac{9}{8}x + (\frac{9}{16})^2 = \frac{99}{8} + (\frac{9}{16})^2$$

$$(x + \frac{9}{16})^2 = \frac{99}{8} + \frac{81}{256} = \frac{3168}{256} + \frac{81}{256} = \frac{3249}{256}$$

$$(x + \frac{9}{16})^2 = (\frac{57}{16})^2$$

$$x + \frac{9}{16} = \frac{57}{16} \qquad \text{or} \qquad x = \frac{57}{16} - \frac{9}{16} = \frac{48}{16}$$

$$x = 3$$

We have found one of the solutions. Knowing this one solution, we can write

$$x^2 + \tfrac{9}{8}x - \tfrac{99}{8} = (x - 3)(x + \text{?}) = 0$$

How do we know the sign in the second factor is a plus sign? Because the product of the second terms in the binomials must be negative and we already have one negative number. The product of -3 and some number must equal $-\tfrac{99}{8}$. Therefore, $-\tfrac{99}{8} \div -3 = \tfrac{33}{8}$ and the other factor is $x + \tfrac{33}{8}$. Setting this equal to zero, we find $x = -\tfrac{33}{8}$, the second solution.

Return to page 99

4

SYSTEMS OF EQUATIONS AND INEQUALITIES

Functions are special relations that exist between two sets. They can be generally defined in terms of mappings.

4.1   Functions

If each element in a nonempty set maps onto one and only one element of another set according to some rule, then a function is defined. The nonempty set is commonly called the *domain* of the function and the other set the *range* of the function. Consider four possibilities of mapping elements of a set onto elements of another set, as shown in Figures 4-1–4-4.

First, in Figure 4-1, we see that each element of the domain is

Figure 4-1

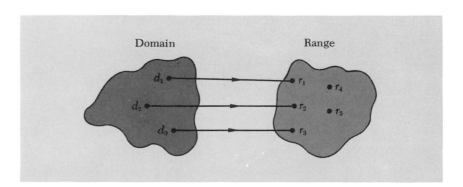

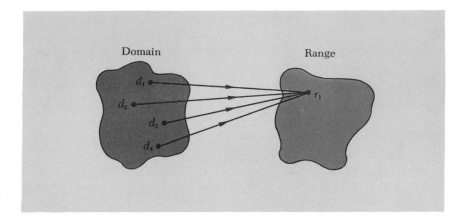

Figure
4-2

mapped onto one and only one element of the range. Figure 4-1 illustrates a function. Note that not all elements of the range have been used. The elements in the range that are mapped onto from the domain are known as *images;* that is, r_1 is the image of d_1, r_2 is the image of d_2, and so forth.

Figure 4-2 also illustrates a function even though there is only one element in its range. Each element of the domain is mapped onto one and only one element of the range. Each element of the domain has one and only one image in the range. This is an example of a *many-to-one* function.

By contrast, Figure 4-3 illustrates a relation that is *not* a function. Here some elements of the domain map onto more than one element of the range. Clearly, d_2 does not have a unique image in the range, since it maps onto both r_1 and r_2.

Figure
4-3

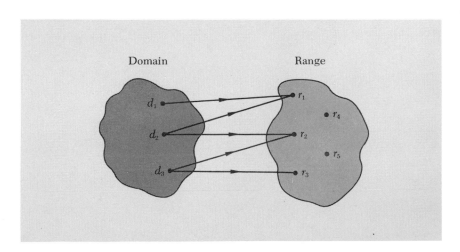

DEFINITION 4-1 ———————————————————————————

A **function** is a relation between two sets D and R such that to each element of the set D, the domain, there corresponds one and only one element of the second set R, the range.

The one-to-one mapping shown in Figure 4-4 is a special kind of function, since *every* element of the range is the image of exactly one element in the domain. Another special kind of function is known as an *onto* function. Figures 4-2 and 4-4 represent *onto* functions, because every element of the range is the image of at least one element of the domain. Figure 4-4 then represents a *one-to-one* function and an *onto* function.

Most of the graphs we have drawn so far have been graphs of functions. As we progress with the development of the concept of function you should try to identify a graph given in a previous chapter that could *not* have represented a function.

When we were plotting the points corresponding to ordered pairs that satisfied the equation $y = x^2$, we were plotting a graph of a function of x. We identified the points in the plane with pairs of real numbers by finding the value of y corresponding to a particular value of x. A table of ordered pairs was found as follows:

x	0	1	2	3	−1	−2	−3
y	0	1	4	9	1	4	9

Figure 4-4

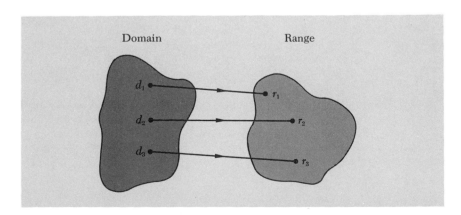

Domain   Range

d_1

d_2

d_3

r_1

r_2

r_3

For each value of x we found exactly one value of y that satisfied the condition imposed by the equation $y = x^2$. In such a situation, we say that y *is a function of* x, because each value of x (an element of the domain) has a unique image in the set of values of y (the range).

On close inspection of the table, we notice that for all but one of the values of y there correspond two values of x; when $y = 4$, for example, $x = 2$ or $x = -2$. For this reason we say that x is *not* a function of y.

The graphs of the linear equations we have considered were also graphs of functions. To show this, let us consider the equation $y = 3x + 1$ and its graph as shown in Figure 4-5. Both the equation and its graph clearly show that for any value of x, a unique y, representing the second coordinate, is determined which satisfies the equation, and which, in turn, provides us with an ordered pair (x, y) representing a point on the graph. This is in harmony with our definition of a function, and we conclude that y is a function of x. However, if we solve the equation for x and write it in the form $x = \frac{1}{3}(y - 1)$, we note that this equation expresses x as a function of y. This is also in harmony with our definition of a function because for any value of y a unique value of x is determined.

If we know in a given situation that y is a function of x, we commonly use the notation

$$y = f(x)$$

which is read "y equals f of x." This is simply an abbreviation for saying "y is a function of x." For example, in considering the equa-

Figure 4-5

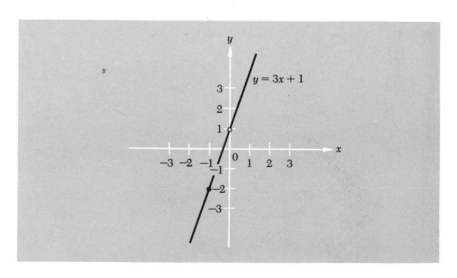

tion $y = 3x + 1$ we can write

$$y = f(x) = 3x + 1$$

Now, instead of always seeking the corresponding value of y for a given value of x, we shorten the discussion to the simple directive, "find $f(6)$." We find $f(6)$ by substituting 6 for x in the equation. Thus, $f(6) = 3 \cdot 6 + 1 = 19$. We say, then, for the function f, as defined by the equation $y = 3x + 1$, with domain equal to the set of real number replacements for x, that we can write

$$
\begin{aligned}
f(0) &= 3(0) + 1 = 1 \\
f(3) &= 3(3) + 1 = 10 \\
f(-\tfrac{1}{2}) &= 3(-\tfrac{1}{2}) + 1 = -\tfrac{1}{2} \\
f(-6) &= 3(-6) + 1 = -17
\end{aligned}
$$

We have found the corresponding values of y for the values of $x = 0, 3, -\tfrac{1}{2}, -6$.

If we view the equation $x = \tfrac{1}{3}(y - 1)$ as expressing x as a function of y, this function is different from the function f just defined, even through both functions have the set of real numbers as their domain and range and both are derived from the same original equation. The functions are different, because the rule for determining the image of a given value of the domain has been changed. Our first function was $f(x) = 3x + 1$, where $y = f(x)$. We call our second function F to show that it is different from f. That is, we let $F(y) = \tfrac{1}{3}(y - 1)$, where $x = F(y)$.

Figure 4-6 shows the graph of another function, which we call g.

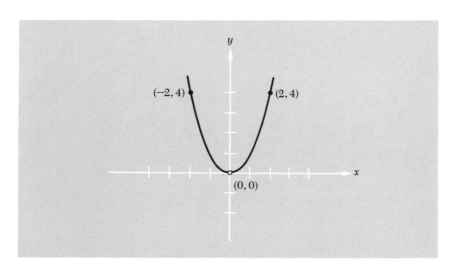

We see that $g(x) = x^2$, which we have shown earlier as the graph of the equation $y = x^2$. Examining Figure 4-6, we see that no two points on the curve have coordinates with identical abscissas. That is, no two points have coordinates with the same first element. It is useful to realize the following alternate definition:

DEFINITION 4-2 ───

A set of ordered pairs of real numbers with no two of the pairs having the same first component is a **function**.

───

Hence, a graph of a function of x never has more than one intersection with any vertical line. Check this by imagining vertical lines drawn in Figure 4-6.

Test your understanding of the ideas and vocabulary introduced thus far in this chapter by doing the following exercises:

1. Find two elements of the range of the function G if $G(x) = -5x - 3$ and the domain of G is the set of integers.

2. Let D be $\{2, 4, 6\}$ and let R be the set of odd integers. Define a function whose domain is D and whose range is R.

3. The function H assigns to each point on the globe a number representing the altitude with respect to sea level in feet. Determine the domain and range of H.

4. Given the function $h(x) = x^2 - x + 2$, find $h(0)$, $h(-3)$, and $h(\frac{1}{2})$.

5. In a half filled auditorium, a relation that is a function can be established between the people and the seats. Find the domain and range of this function.

6. In a one hundred question examination, a relation may be established between the number of correct answers and the grades of A, B, C, D, and F, which were assigned by the instructor. State such a relation so that it is a function.

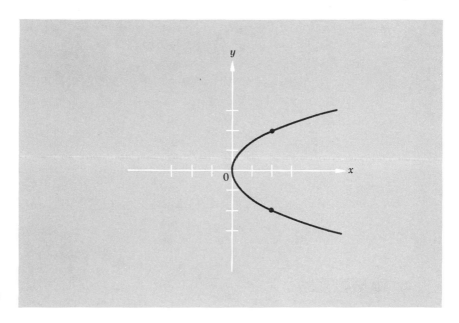

**Figure
4-7**

7. How do we know that Figure 4-7 does not represent a function
   of x? Does it represent a function of y?

CHECK YOUR WORK on page 152

4.2   The Function Game

The basic ideas and vocabulary of functions have now been discussed. However, because many students have a difficult time grasp-
ing the concept of a function, let us relate it to what you may soon be
teaching in the elementary school.

Many teachers today play a game generally referred to as "what's
my rule?" to illustrate the concept of a function. In its simplest form,
the teacher asks a pupil to name a number. The teacher writes this
number on the board, mentally applies a rule, and writes a second
number beside the one given by the child. This process always applying the same rule is continued until a pupil indicates that he
knows the rule. This pupil then takes the place of the teacher to
demonstrate that he has discovered the correct rule, and after a few
more examples of the application of the rule he then explains the
rule to the class.

For example, if the pupil names the numbers 1, 6, 7, and 9, and the teacher writes a number after each of them as follows:

1	2
6	7
7	8
9	10

The rule "add 1 to each number" is soon discovered.

In later grades, the rule may be more sophisticated than the simple rules to which the first grade teacher might be limited, but the procedure is the same. A game played by a sixth grade class might go as follows:

Child says: "Three."

Teacher writes: "3   9."

Child says: "Minus one."

Teacher writes: "−1   1."

Child says: "Zero."

Teacher writes: "0   3."

This continues until the teacher has written the following table on the board:

3	9
−1	1
0	3
1	5
2	7
4	11

At this point the teacher stops and tells the class that with this much information she feels that they should be able to figure out her rule. See if you can find her rule before reading further.

After some study a pupil indicates that he thinks he knows the rule. Another pupil names the number $\frac{1}{2}$. The first pupil writes $\frac{1}{2}$ and then 4. Minutes later, several of the class have the answer and the teacher asks the first pupil for the rule.

He says, "The rule is 'you add 3 to the number and then to that result you add the number.'" He writes this on the board: "$N+3+N$."

Another child says he has used a different rule: "$2N+3$."

A third pupil says, "Those are the same rules!"

And so it goes. We note that this game carefully defines a function. The teacher first decides on a rule, applies it to an element of the domain selected by a pupil, and then writes its image. The pupils try to figure out the rule and then apply it. In our example, the pupils who had first discovered the two "different" rules would then explain how they had discovered their rules. In this case, one pupil had rewritten the data as follows

-1	0	1	2	3	4
1	3	5	7	9	11

A condensed report of his thinking might have been: "Well, 3 is 3 more than 0, and 5 is 3 more than 1 plus 1, and 7 is 3 more than 2 plus 2. So the rule is 'you take the number, add 3, and then add the number,' or just 'double the number and add 3.'"

To further clarify the concept of a function, let us examine the calendar for this particular month. What relation exists between the numerals on the calendar and the set of days of the week? Can you define a function using these two sets? For Wednesday, does there correspond one and only one numeral on the calendar? No. There is no unique image in the set of numerals for any day of the week.

Does there correspond one and only one day of the week for every numeral on the calendar? Yes. We see that the numeral 5 corresponds to one and only one day of the week. To what day of the week does the numeral 22 correspond? What day of the week is the image of the numeral 26? Now define the function in your own words.

EXERCISES
4.2

1. Let O be the set of odd integers greater than zero, and E the set of even integers greater than zero. Give a function whose domain is O and range is E. Give a function whose domain is E and range is O.

2. Define an *onto* function for O onto E for the sets you defined in problem 1.

3. Give an example of a relation that is not a function.

4. Map the function pictorially that you defined in the discussion of this month's calendar. Would you associate your mapping with Figure 4-1, 4-2, 4-3, or 4-4?

5. Given $g(x) = x^2 - 3x + 5$, find $g(-5)$, $g(-1)$, and $g(\frac{1}{2})$.

6. Given $H(x) = (-x)^2 + 3x$, find $H(3)$, $H(-3)$, and $H(\frac{1}{2})$.

7. If A is the set of number pairs $\{(r, t)\}$ representing rate and time, and D is the set of numbers representing distance, can you define a function between these two sets?

8. Find the rule that dictates the second element in the following groups of ordered pairs:

    a. $(3, 5), (8, 10), (-3, -1), (-1, 1), (11, 13)$;
    b. $(0, 0), (1, 2), (3, 6), (5, 10), (12, 24)$;
    c. $(2, -1), (6, 3), (-2, -5), (1, -2), (57, 54)$;
    d. $(1, 3), (5, 11), (7, 15), (0, 1), (-1, -1), (-4, -7)$.

4.3 Graphing Systems of Equations

We are now prepared to examine a system of equations. Consider the two polynomials $x^2 + 2x - 8$ and $2x + 1$. We express these polynomials as functions by writing $f(x) = x^2 + 2x - 8$ and $g(x) = 2x + 1$. For graphing purposes we set both functions equal to y and obtain the equations

$$y = x^2 + 2x - 8 \tag{1}$$

$$y = 2x + 1 \tag{2}$$

To plot the first equation, we see by inspection that the y intercept must be -8. (If you have forgotten, stop and figure out how to do this.) Factoring the function f, we find it equals $(x - 2)(x + 4)$; so the x intercepts are $(2, 0)$ and $(-4, 0)$. We have quickly obtained the three ordered pairs $(0, -8)$, $(2, 0)$, and $(-4, 0)$. (How can we tell just from these three points that x is not a function of y?)

Let us plot at least two more points to insure a more accurate drawing of the curve. Can we find the vertex of this parabola? Intuitively, we see, from the graphs of the parabolas we have considered so far, that the vertex always lies at a value of x half-way between the x intercepts $+2$ and -4; in other words, at the point $(-1, y)$. Let us find $f(-1)$.

$$f(-1) = (-1)^2 + 2(-1) - 8 = 1 - 2 - 8 = -9$$

Hence, the vertex lies at the point $(-1, -9)$. Arbitrarily selecting an x value of 3, let us find a fifth point according to the rule established.

$$f(3) = (3)^2 + 2 \cdot 3 - 8 = 9 + 6 - 8 = 15 - 8 = 7$$

So $(3, 7)$ is a point on the curve. We now plot these five points and connect them with a smooth curve. Finally, we plot three points of equation (2) and connect them. The five points we have found so far and the curves connecting them are shown in Figure 4-8.

Figure
4-8

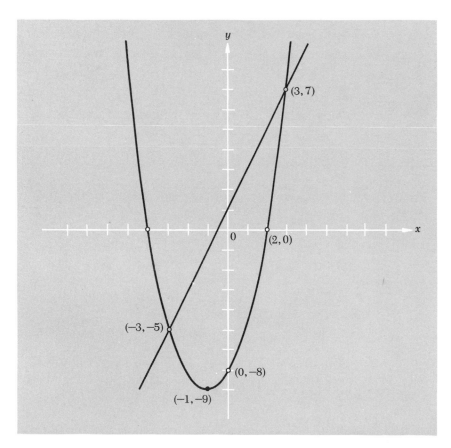

Now if our project were to find the set of ordered pairs that satisfies *either* equation (1) or equation (2), we would state our solution set as all those points lying on the parabola *or* on the straight line in Figure 4-8. In mathematical terms we could write the solution as

$$\{(x, y)|y = x^2 + 2x - 8\} \cup \{(x, y)|y = 2x + 1\}$$

When we seek the set of pairs that satisfy both equation (1) *and* equation (2), we are seeking the intersection of the two solution sets of the equations. Such solutions are called *simultaneous solutions*. The set of equations or conditions for which simultaneous solutions are sought is known as a *system of simultaneous equations*.

Because Figure 4-8 is accurately drawn, we can guess at the simultaneous solutions to the system of equations graphed in the figure. From the directions of the line and parabola, we conclude that they intersect at only two points. The points $(-3, -5)$ and $(3, 7)$ are easily confirmed as solutions of both functions. We therefore conclude that

$$\{(x, y)|y = x^2 + 2x - 8\} \cap \{(x, y)|y = 2x + 1\} = \{(-3, -5), (3, 7)\}$$

EXERCISES
4.3

Find the simultaneous solutions for the following pairs of equations.

1. $y = x + 3$,
   $y = 3 - x$

2. $y = x$,
   $y = 3$

3. $y = 2x + 1$,
   $2y = -x - 3$

4. $x + y = 2$,
   $3y = 4x - 1$

5. $y = x^2 - 1$,
   $y - x = 1$

6. $y = x^2 + 2x + 1$,
   $x + 3 = y$

4.4 Algebraic Solutions of Systems of Equations

Graphing systems of simultaneous equations does not always provide us with such ready, accurate solutions. Let us now consider the problem of the farmer, his cows, and how fast his grass grows (see p. 39). In this problem 10 cows ate in 12 days 3 inches of grass plus by whatever amount the grass grew in 12 days. This relation can be expressed as 10 cows times 12 days equals 3 inches plus 12 times the rate the grass grew per day, or

$$120 \text{ cow-days} = 3 \text{ in.} + (12 \text{ days})(r \text{ in./day}) \tag{1}$$

Also given was that 20 cows in 5 days ate 3 inches plus the grass that grew during 5 days, or

$$100 \text{ cow-days} = 3 \text{ in.} + (5 \text{ days})(r \text{ in./day}) \tag{2}$$

We now seek simultaneous solutions to the system of equations (1) and (2). To facilitate matters, let us change our equations to exhibit 1 cow-day value in each. Dividing equation (1) by 120, we find

$$1 \text{ cow-day} = (\tfrac{1}{40} + \tfrac{1}{10}r) \text{ in./day} \tag{1a}$$

Dividing equation (2) by 100, we find

$$1 \text{ cow-day} = (\tfrac{3}{100} + \tfrac{1}{20}r) \text{ in./day} \tag{2a}$$

If we carefully graph these two equations, plotting values of r on the x axis and cow-days on the y axis, we obtain Figure 4-9.

Figure 4-9

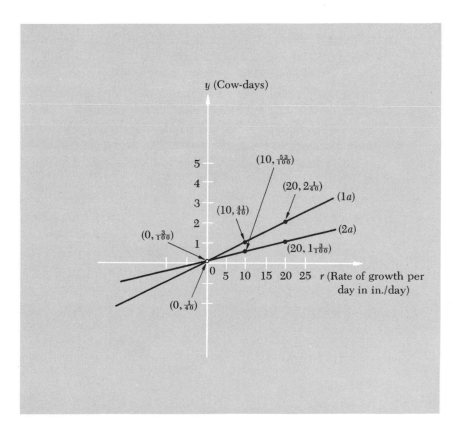

We see from the graph that the intersection of the two lines is a point very close to that representing a rate of zero. We know the answer is a positive fraction because line (1a is above line (2a) at $f(0)$; that is, $\frac{3}{100} > \frac{1}{40}$. But even this much information from the graph does not make finding the *exact* solution easier.

Here again the power of algebra can be appreciated. Since the right-hand members of equations (1a) and (2a) are equal to 1 cowday, the two members are equal to each other by the transitive property of equality. Thus,

$$\frac{1}{40} + \frac{1}{10}r = \frac{3}{100} + \frac{1}{20}r$$

$5 + 20r = 6 + 10r$	(multiplying through by 200)
$10r = 1$	(collecting terms)
$r = \frac{1}{10}$	

We have found that the grass grows at the rate of exactly $\frac{1}{10}$ of an inch per day. Algebraically, there are several ways of solving such a system of simultaneous equations.

First, we know if we write a linear equation in the form $y = mx + k$, the slope of the line is m. Given two such equations with different slopes, the lines will have one and only one intersection point, and the simultaneous solution is found immediately. In the cases of equations (1a) and (2a), we see the slopes are $\frac{1}{10}$ and $\frac{1}{20}$, respectively; hence, the lines must intersect at exactly one point. When dealing with two linear equations, our goal is to combine the two equations in such a way as to eliminate one of the unknowns.

Let us investigate two different methods of solving a system of simultaneous equations by solving a hypothetical problem. (Read carefully now!) Suppose you are in the business of buying wams, modifying them, and selling wims. As it develops, when you sell 6 wims and buy 1 wam, you have 24 more dollars in your pocket than before the transactions were made. But when you sell only 2 wims and buy 5 wams, you discover you have 20 dollars less. The problem is to find the going price of the wims and wams.

First, we translate these two sentences into equations. From the first sentence we obtain

$$6x - y = 24 \tag{3}$$

(where x is the price of wims, y is the price of wams), and from the second sentence we can write

$$2x - 5y = -20 \tag{4}$$

Method I: Graphing

Solving the equations for y, we obtain

$$y = 6x - 24 \tag{3a}$$

$$y = \tfrac{2}{5}x + 4 \tag{4a}$$

From these two equations we see that the slopes differ; consequently, there is one intersection point. With careful plotting, the intersection is easily seen to be $(5, 6)$. Thus, a wim sells for $5.00 and a wam costs $6.00. (See Figure 4-10.)

This answer tells us a little more about *you* and your business of wims and wams. Either you have a case of the wim-wams and are rapidly losing money; or, more reasonably, you somehow are able to obtain more than one wim from each wam through the modification process. But since this is a hypothetical problem anyway, we need not know which of the two alternatives is true.

Figure 4-10

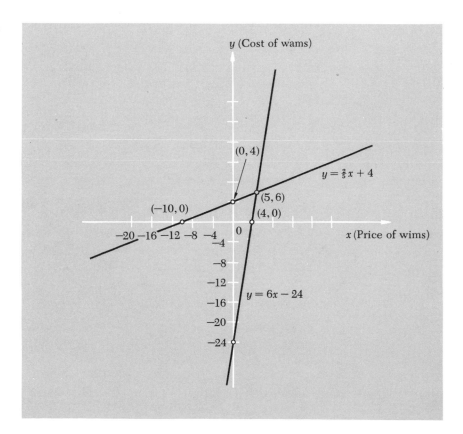

Method II: Combining the Two Equations Algebraically

This method offers several avenues of approach.

1. We can capitalize on the transitive property of equality as we did earlier. Since we have already solved both equations for y, as seen in equations (3a) and (4a), we can equate the right-hand members of each equation

$$6x - 24 = \tfrac{2}{5}x + 4$$
$$30x - 120 = 2x + 20 \qquad \text{(multiplying through by 5)}$$
$$28x = 140$$
$$x = 5$$

Substituting this value of x in equation (3a) we obtain for y

$$y = 6 \cdot 5 - 24 = 30 - 24 = 6$$

Again we find wims selling for $5 each, while wams cost $6 each.

2. Many times the quickest way to solve a system of equations is by direct substitution. Since it is easy to solve equation (1) for y, since $y = 6x - 24$, we can substitute this value for y in equation (2) and obtain

$$2x - 5(6x - 24) = -20$$
$$2x - 30x + 120 = -20$$
$$-28x = -140$$
$$x = 5$$

Therefore $y = 30 - 24 = 6$, or the price of a wam is $6.00.

3. Do you remember the cancellation property of addition, which states that if $a + x = b + x$, then $a = b$? Another way of viewing this property is that we can subtract equals from equals. For example, since $x = x$, we can subtract x from both sides of the equation $a + x = b + x$ and obtain $a = b$ as follows:

$$\begin{array}{rcl} a + x &=& b + x \\ -x = & & -x \\ \hline a &=& b \end{array}$$

Often simultaneous equations can be rewritten in an equivalent form so that one may be subtracted from another to obtain a third equation having one less variable. Consider the following case:

$$6x - y = 24 \tag{5}$$

$$2x - 5y = -20 \tag{6}$$

We can obtain a coefficient of 5 for y in equation (5) simply by multiplying equation (5) by 5. Now we have

$$30x - 5y = 120$$
$$\underline{2x - 5y = -20}$$

If we subtract the second of these equations from the first, we obtain

$$28x \quad = 140$$

which is a linear equation in one variable and can easily be solved to yield $x = 5$.

It would have been just as easy to multiply equation (5) by -5:

$$-30x + 5y = -120$$

to which we could *add* equation (6)

$$\underline{2x - 5y = \quad -20}$$

The sum of these equations is

$$-28x \quad = -140$$

and again we find that $x = 5$.

EXERCISES
4.4

Find the solution sets for the following systems of linear equations by graphing, by direct substitution, and by combining the two equations into one equation. (The brace in front of the equations is standard notation for a system of simultaneous equations.)

1. $\begin{cases} x = y + 1 \\ x + y = -5 \end{cases}$ 2. $\begin{cases} x + y = 3 \\ \frac{1}{2}x = \frac{1}{5}y + 5 \end{cases}$

Find the solution set the quickest way you can:

3. $\begin{cases} x - y = 1 \\ y + 3x = -3 \end{cases}$ 6. $\begin{cases} 3x - 2y = 6 \\ 7x + 4y = -12 \end{cases}$

4. $\begin{cases} 2x - y = 3 \\ y = 3x - 5 \end{cases}$ 7. $\begin{cases} 2x - 3y = 3 \\ 3y = 2x + 12 \end{cases}$

5. $\begin{cases} 2y = \frac{3}{2}x - 10 \\ 3x = 20 + 4y \end{cases}$ 8. $\begin{cases} 3x + 4y = -11 \\ 5x - 2y = 1 \end{cases}$

4.5 Types of Systems of Equations

A few words about problems 4 and 5 in the preceding exercises. If you graphed the two equations in problem 4, what sort of picture would you obtain? Since both lines have a slope of $\frac{2}{3}$, your graph would show two separate and distinct but parallel lines with positive slopes, one intersecting the y axis at 4 and the other at -1. Such a system of equations is known as an *inconsistent system*. The name is fitting, since if you subtracted one equation from the other after first solving for y (see answer to problem 4), you would obtain $0 = -1 - 4$, which is, to say the least, an inconsistent result. Since the lines are parallel, the solution set is the null set. It is worth noting that a contradiction (an inconsistent result) always arises when an inconsistent system of two linear equations is solved algebraically.

In problem 5, if you multiply the first equation by 2, you see that the two equations are equivalent. If you arrange the terms in the same order and subtract, you obtain $0 = 0$. If you graph the two equations, you find that they represent the same line. Such a system is known as a *dependent system*. Algebraically, solving a system of two dependent linear equations always leads to $0 = 0$. Since the lines are the same, the solution set is always the set of numbers (x, y), which satisfy the equation of the line. As you have probably guessed, a system which is neither inconsistent nor dependent is known as an *independent and consistent system*.

We have seen that a system of two linear equations in two unknowns is always one of the following:

1. An *independent system*, for which exactly one ordered pair of numbers exists in the solution set (the lines picturing the equations have only one point of intersection).

2. A *dependent system*, in which the two equations are equivalent and the solution set is an infinite set of ordered pairs (the two lines are the same).

3. An *inconsistent system*, which has no ordered pair in the solution set, therefore the solution set is the null set (the two lines are parallel).

Now let us examine algebraic approaches to the solution of a system involving a quadratic equation. Study Figure 4-8 on page 129 again. This figure graphically portrays the solution set for the system of equations:

$$\begin{cases} x^2 + 2x - 8 = y & (1) \\ 2x + 1 = y & (2) \end{cases}$$

To solve these equations algebraically, we could easily employ either the subtraction or the direct substitution method. Subtracting equation (2) from equation (1), we obtain the difference $x^2 - 9 = 0$. We immediately recognize the left-hand member of this equation as the difference of two squares $(x^2 - 3^2)$, and therefore we can write its factors as $(x + 3)$ and $(x - 3)$. We now have $(x + 3)(x - 3) = 0$, and thus $x = -3$, or $x = +3$. To find the values of y, we substitute each of these values of x in equation (2).

$$y = -6 + 1 = -5 \qquad \text{(when } x = -3)$$
$$y = 6 + 1 = 7 \qquad \text{(when } x = +3)$$

Hence the solution set (the set of intersection points of the two graphs, or the set of simultaneous solutions of the system) is $\{(-3, -5), (3, 7)\}$. This is confirmed by examining Figure 4-8.

By the direct substitution method, we substitute in equation (1) the value of y given in equation (2) and find

$$x^2 + 2x - 8 = 2x + 1$$
$$x^2 + (2x - 2x) + (-8 - 1) = 0$$
$$x^2 - 9 = 0$$

Again we obtain the solution set $\{(-3, -5), (3, 7)\}$.

Systems consisting of quadratic and linear equations do not always lend themselves so readily to solution, but having the computational skill necessary to solve more complicated systems is not a necessary prerequisite for an understanding of the various possible results. In the above system there were obviously two points of intersection. Is this always the case? Try to graph two other possible results you might obtain when solving a system consisting of a quadratic and a linear equation, both limited to two unknowns. *After* you have spent time on this problem (you should find at least two more different results),

CHECK YOUR WORK on page 153

Since you have studied the pages for the last checking your work section, do you see how much more complicated are the possibilities when we move from a system of two linear equations to a system of a quadratic equation and a linear equation? If you do, that is good, because an appreciation and understanding of another type of system of equations is the purpose of this discussion.

EXERCISES
4.5

Consider the following equations:

a. $y^2 = x$ 　　　　　d. $y - x = 1$
b. $y = x - 2$ 　　　　e. $y + x + 2(1 - x) = 0$
c. $x = -2$

1. In which category—independent, dependent, inconsistent— does each of the following systems belong? Use both graphing and algebraic solution methods in determining your answers.

   a. Equations (a) and (c).　　d. Equations (a) and (b).
   b. Equations (c) and (d).　　e. Equations (b) and (e).
   c. Equations (c) and (e).　　f. Equations (b) and (c).

2. Find the solution set for each system in problem 1.

4.6 Systems of More Than Two Equations

Since we have limited the discussion thus far to systems of only two equations, you may wonder if all systems must be so limited. This is not the case. A system may have as many equations as we need or desire. In general, a solution set containing a unique element can be obtained for an independent and consistent system of linear equations *if the number of equations is equal to the number of unknowns.*

Let us illustrate this by solving a system of three linear equations in three unknowns. (We could make it 23 equations in 23 unknowns, but again our purpose is to gain understanding and knowledge of the concepts involved rather than extensive computational skills.) Consider the system

$$\begin{cases} x - y + z = -1 & (1) \\ x + y + 2z = 2 & (2) \\ x - 5y + 3z = -7 & (3) \end{cases}$$

We have already solved a system of two linear equations in two unknowns; therefore, if we can somehow reduce these three equations in three unknowns to two equations in two unknowns, we can solve the system. Notice that each of the three equations involves a term of $1 \cdot x$. If we subtract equation (1) from equation (2), we obtain a new equation involving only the variables y and z. Similarly, if we subtract equation (3) from equation (1), we find still another equation involving only y and z. This process reduces the three equations to two equations in two unknowns. Let us proceed.

$$2y + z = 3 \qquad \text{(equation (2) minus equation (1))} \qquad (4)$$

and

$$4y - 2z = 6 \qquad \text{(equation (1) minus equation (3))} \qquad (5)$$

Multiplying equation (4) by 2 and adding this to equation (5), we obtain

$$8y = 12 \qquad \text{or} \qquad y = \tfrac{3}{2}$$

Substituting this value of y in equation (4), we have

$$2 \cdot \tfrac{3}{2} + z = 3$$
$$3 + z = 3$$
$$z = 0$$

Having found the values $y = \tfrac{3}{2}$ and $z = 0$, we substitute them into equation (1) to find

$$x - \tfrac{3}{2} + 0 = -1$$
$$x = \tfrac{3}{2} - 1$$
$$x = \tfrac{1}{2}$$

The unique element of our solution set is now seen to be the ordered triplet $(\tfrac{1}{2}, \tfrac{3}{2}, 0)$.

Lacking graphical confirmation of our solution, you should verify that it is a member of the solution set of each of the three equations by substituting these values for x, y, z in *each* of the three equations. (Does $\{-1, 1, 1\}$ satisfy equations (1) and (2)?) We cannot graph this system on Cartesian coordinates because three variables are present. Such systems *can* be graphed in a coordinate system of three variables, but this is beyond the scope of this text.

We conclude that the procedures we used to solve our system of three equations are basically the same as those we used to solve a system of two linear equations. Which procedure is the quickest or surest depends on the system and the form of the equations. The point is that the underlying logic is the same — we combine both equations (1) and (2) to obtain equation (4), a new equation with one less variable. We repeat this with a different pair, equations (1) and (3), to obtain equation (5). We have successfully reduced the number of equations and the number of variables. We repeat this process until we obtain a linear equation in one unknown. Substitution of the value for this unknown in one of the last two equations used yields the value of the second variable. This process is continued until all variables have been found.

EXERCISES
4.6

Find the ordered pairs (x, y) and ordered triplets (x, y, z) that are elements of the solution sets for each of the following.

1. $$\begin{cases} x + y + z = 4 \\ -2x + y - z = 1 \\ -x - 2y + 2z = 3 \end{cases}$$

3. $$\begin{cases} x + y + z = 6 \\ 2x + y - z = -2 \\ 3x - 2y + 3z = 8 \end{cases}$$

2. $$\begin{cases} x - y + z = 0 \\ 4x + 3y - z = -8 \\ x + 5y + 3z = 12 \end{cases}$$

4. $$\begin{cases} y^2 = 2x \\ 2y = x \end{cases}$$

5. $$\begin{cases} x^2 = y + z \\ x + y + z = 6 \\ 4x = 2y + z \end{cases}$$

6. Construct and solve your own independent and consistent system of four equations in four unknowns. (Hint: Graph four lines having a common point of intersection.)

4.7 Systems Involving Inequalities

The relations "is greater than," "is less than," "is greater than or equal to," and "is less than or equal to" all occur frequently in everyday problems.

If you have thirty desks in your room, you can seat a number of children equal to or less than thirty. If a manufacturer of machine parts is given a tolerance of $\pm$ five-thousandths of an inch, he knows that a dimension of a 1 in. part (call it x) must be equal to or greater than $1\frac{995}{1000}$ in. and equal to or less than $1\frac{5}{1000}$ in. We write his acceptable measurement of x as $\frac{995}{1000} \le x \le \frac{1005}{1000}$ or $0.995 \le x \le 1.005$.

In the problem of the oil company on page 39, the requirement that *at least* 1000 barrels of jet fuel a day be produced to satisfy a contract with a commercial airline is actually a requirement that an amount equal to or greater than 1000 barrels a day be produced. Similarly, the fact that the maximum production capability per day was 10,000 barrels implied only that the company could daily produce a number of barrels equal to or less than 10,000.

When a husband tells his wife (or begs her, as the case may be) not to spend more than $80.00 on a coat, he means she can spend an amount equal to or less than $80.00. Whereas, given a little rationalization and a good salesman, the wife might mentally reverse the sign and visualize "one coat $\geq$ $80.00"; naturally, only trouble can result.

The number of everyday situations that can be translated into mathematical statements of inequalities like the above examples are countless. Therefore, we should carefully examine the uses of inequalities in problem solving. Since so much of our work with conditions of equality has been clarified through graphing, we can logically expect that graphing of inequalities yields similar clarification.

What would an inequality look like if graphed? Let us discover the answer for ourselves. Consider the inequality $x + 2y > 5$, and let us proceed from what we know. We can plot the condition $x + 2y = 5$ as shown in Figure 4-11. The resulting line divides the plane into the following three disjoint sets: points on the line, points above the line, and points below the line. This partitioning can be illustrated

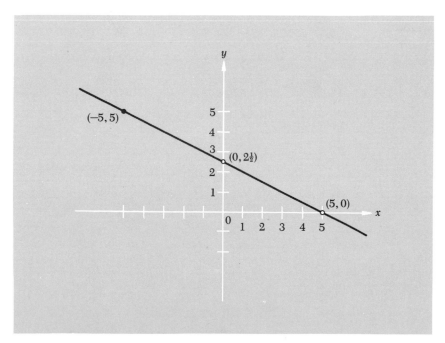

by using the *trichotomy law* of the real number system; i.e., the co-ordinates of any one point must be a solution set of one and only one of the following conditions:

$$x + 2y = 5 \qquad x + 2y < 5 \qquad x + 2y > 5$$

We know that the locus of the first condition is the set of points on the line itself. Which set of points do we associate with the second and third conditions? Since each point must belong to one and only one of the sets, let us take a point not on the line and see how we associate it. Consider the point $(0, 0)$. Substitution of these values for x and y in the three conditions shows it to be only a solution to the second condition.

Similarly, the coordinates of a point above the line, such as $(0, 5)$, are seen to satisfy only the third condition; so we say that for this example "greater than" refers to the points above the line in question. We agree that the solution set for the condition $x + 2y > 5$ are graphed as shown in Figure 4-12. Since the points on the line $x + 2y = 5$ are not in the area described by $x + 2y > 5$, the line is shown in dashed form. The shaded area is the graph of the condition $x + 2y > 5$, and is known as an *open half-plane* because it does not include the points on the line that forms its boundary.

A *closed half-plane* is represented as in Figure 4-12 except that the

Figure 4-12

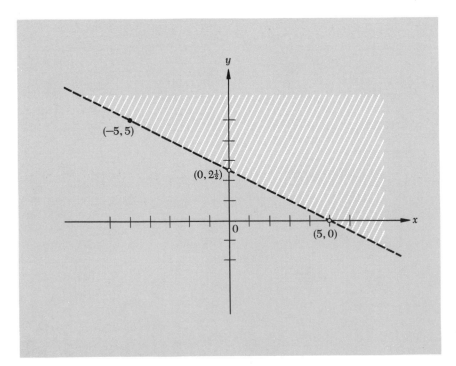

line is drawn solid rather than dashed. The union of the set of points on a line and the set of points in the open half-plane it describes is called a *closed half-plane.* Using mathematical symbols, we say $x + 2y \geqq 5$ describes a closed half-plane. Any straight line divides the plane of the Cartesian coordinate system into three mutually disjoint sets—the line and two open half-planes.

Let us now consider a system of simultaneous linear conditions of inequality by finding the solution set for the following system:

$$\begin{cases} x + 2y \geqq 5 \\ y \leqq x - 1 \end{cases}$$

In mathematical terminology, we can, of course, write the solution set as

$$\{(x, y) | x, y \in R, x + 2y \geqq 5 \ and \ y \leqq x - 1\}$$

This, however, does not help us visualize the solution any more than a sheet of music helps the ordinary musician hear the orchestration. We again resort to graphing to help us. We graph the first condition as in Figure 4-12 but with a solid line, since we are considering the *closed* half-plane described by $x + 2y \geqq 5$. Now we superimpose our graph of the second condition as shown in Figure 4-13. Note that since our second condition involves "equal to or less

Figure 4-13

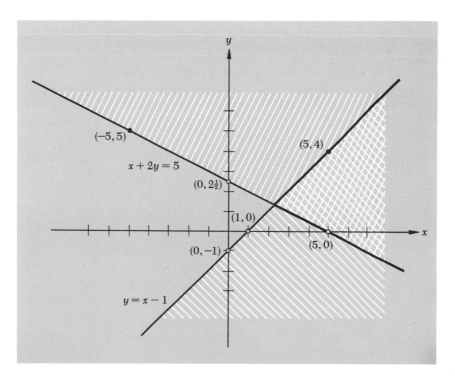

than," the closed half-plane is formed by the union of the line and the space *below* it.

In Figure 4-13 the solution set for the system stands out clearly as the intersection of the two sets. The intersection is the set of points that lie in the cross-shaded area and on the heavily drawn rays. Thus, any point lying on the heavily drawn rays or in the cross-shaded area is a point whose coordinates satisfy both of the required conditions.

We found earlier that the coordinates of a point below a line satisfied the condition "is less than." We were then talking about a particular condition. *Is that statement true for any condition "is less than"?* Let us find out.

Graph the line corresponding to $x - y = 0$. Now consider the condition $x - y \leq 0$, and show this on your graph. Select a point *below* the line on your graph — say $(4, 0)$. Does the ordered pair $(4, 0)$ satisfy the condition $x - y \leq 0$?

Your answer should be "no." But consider in this case *how* we can plot inequalities in a consistent manner and still be accurate? There *is* a condition we can impose that permits us to say with confidence that any point satisfying an inequality lies below the line for the relation "is less than" and above the line for "is greater than." Experiment with several lines and open half-planes, and develop the condition we must impose. Do not attempt the following exercises until you

CHECK YOUR WORK on page 155

EXERCISES
4.7

1. Graph the following inequalities:

   a. $x + y \leq 5$ c. $-y < 2x - 1$

   b. $y \geq x + 1$ d. $5 > 3x - y$

2. Graphically illustrate the solution sets of the following systems:

   a. $\begin{cases} y \leq x + 2 \\ y \geq x - 1 \end{cases}$ c. $\begin{cases} x + y < 4 \\ 2x + y \geq 2 \end{cases}$

   b. $\begin{cases} x + y \leq 2 \\ x \geq -2 \\ y \geq -1 \end{cases}$ d. $\begin{cases} y \geq x + 2 \\ y < 3 \\ y \geq -x \end{cases}$

3. Graphically portray the solution set of pairs of real numbers (x, y) such that their sum when rounded to the nearest integer is 2. (Round 0.5 up to 1.)

4.8 Linear Programing

This brief introduction to the concepts of graphing linear conditions is sufficient to enable you to solve the problem of the oil company (page 39). We recall that restrictions were placed on the company by previous commitments, by the number of trucks owned, and by limitations on daily production. These restrictions are commonly called *constraints*. The constraints can be reduced to:

1. At least 1000 barrels of gasoline must be produced daily.

2. A minimum of 2000 barrels of jet fuel must be produced daily.

3. Not more than 10,000 barrels of gasoline and jet fuel can be produced daily.

4. Not more than 210,000 barrel-miles are available daily.

You recall that the profit per barrel was 20¢ for gas and 10¢ for jet fuel, and that the problem was to determine the production combination providing the highest profit. If x is the number of barrels of gasoline and y the number of barrels of jet fuel, we can reduce the above constraints to the following system of inequalities:

$$\begin{cases} x \geq 1000 & (1) \\ y \geq 2000 & (2) \\ x + y \leq 10{,}000 & (3) \\ 30x + 10y \leq 210{,}000 & (4) \end{cases}$$

The first three conditions are obvious. The fourth condition warrants some discussion. Recall that gasoline was to be hauled 30 miles and jet fuel 10 miles. Therefore, if we haul x barrels of gasoline 30 miles, we use up $30x$ barrel-miles. Similarly, if we haul y barrels of jet fuel 10 miles, we use up $10y$ barrel-miles. The sum of these two expressions must not exceed 210,000 barrel-miles. Hence,

$$30x + 10y \leq 210{,}000$$

Graphing the four conditions, we obtain the four-sided polygon, shown in Figure 4-14, as the solution to the system.

We know from a basic theorem of linear programing that the maximum and minimum values are found at two of the four corners of the polygon. If we identify these points, and evaluate the profit from that proportion of production of the two fuels, we will find the maximum profit possible and the production figures that will ensure this maximum profit.

Let us find the four corners. Each of the corners results from the intersection of two lines. To identify the intersection, we need only to solve the system of simultaneous linear equations involved. To find point A, we solve the equations $x = 1000$ and $y = 2000$. The intersection of these two lines is shown in Figure 4-14 to be the point (1, 2). (If these were the only two constraints operating, we would shade the area above $y = 2$ and to the right of $x = 1$ and identify the solution set as the cross shaded area.)

Figure 4-14

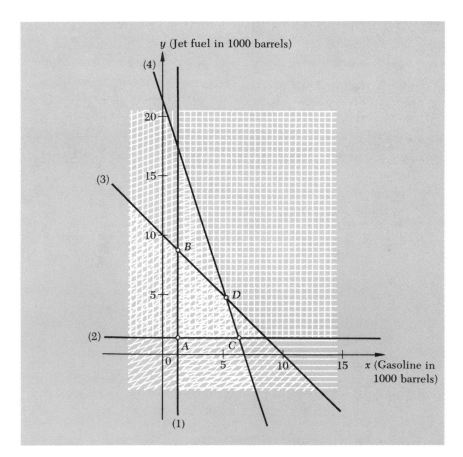

To find point B, we solve for the intersection of lines (1) and (3). Substituting $x = 1000$ in the equation for line (3), we find $1000 + y = 10,000$. Thus, $y = 9000$, and B is the point $(1, 9)$.

Point C is the intersection of lines (2) and (4). By direct substitution of y in equation (4), we find

$$30x + 10 \cdot 2000 = 210,000$$
$$30x = 190,000$$
$$x = \frac{19,000}{3}$$

Thus, C is the point $(\frac{19}{3}, 2)$.

Since D is the intersection of lines (3) and (4), we need to solve the system

$$\begin{cases} x + y = 10,000 \\ 30x + 10y = 210,000 \end{cases}$$

Multiplying the first equation by -10, and then adding the two equations, we find

$$20x = 110,000$$
$$x = 5500$$

Substituting this value in equation (3), we find that $y = 4500$, and D is $(5.5, 4.5)$.

Let us now evaluate the profit gained from each of these production point quotas. Since point A represents the smallest production, we rightfully suspect it to represent the *minimum* profit obtainable within the system of constraints. Let us calculate the profit for the four points at 20¢ per barrel for gasoline and 10¢ per barrel for jet fuel:

At point A: $\quad 1000 \cdot 20$¢ $+ 2000 \cdot 10$¢ $= 200 + 200 = \$400.00$

At point B: $\quad 1000 \cdot 20$¢ $+ 9000 \cdot 10$¢ $= 200 + 900 = \$1,100.00$

At point C: $\quad \frac{1}{3}(19,000) \cdot 20$¢ $+ 2000 \cdot 10$¢ $= 1267 + 200 = \$1,467.00$

At point D: $\quad 5500 \cdot 20$¢ $+ 4500 \cdot 10$¢ $= 1100 + 450 = \$1,550.00$

Consequently, the daily production that yields the highest profit will be 5500 barrels of gasoline and 4500 of jet fuel, and is represented in Figure 4-14 by D.

We should note that all points in the polygon in Figure 4-14 represent production rates of the two fuels which would be *possible* in view of the constraints. What would the profit be at the point $(5, 5)$?

At $(4, 4)$? At $(5, 6)$? Is the point $(7, 3)$ in the polygon? Which constraint prevents us from using this ratio of production? On these five questions,

CHECK YOUR WORK on page 157

EXERCISES
4.8

1. Suppose we are in the business of producing and selling wigs and wahms (these are not to be confused with the *wams* in an earlier problem, besides, wams are brown!). We make these wigs and wahms from wags, and wags cost us $5.00 each. We sell wigs at $4.00 and wahms at $3.00 and we are able to produce exactly 1 wig and 1 wahm from 1 wag. We operate under several constraints. We can buy at most 20 wags a day. We have a contract to sell 4 wahms a day to an undercover spy network, and our machinery can produce only 14 wahms a day that meet specifications. That is, if we produce 20 wigs and 20 wahms a day, the last 6 wahms are ruined by our outdated machinery. What procedure nets us the greatest daily profit?

2. In problem 1, what procedure nets the greatest percentage-of-cost profit?

3. Make up a linear programing problem that you believe would be interesting to a ninth grader or to an especially bright sixth grader.

SUMMARY ————————————————————————————————

In this chapter we have studied the concept of *function*, its meaning, related vocabulary, and some of its relationships within the structure of mathematics. We found that a polynomial in one unknown expresses a function of that unknown. We saw that the graph of a function of x always has exactly one value of y for any value of x and that, therefore, the curve generated by the function never intersects any vertical line at more than one point. We found that a function is a special kind of relation.

We studied the intersections of curves and lines generated by various functions and found once more that we could predict a great deal about the intersections by a close inspection of the functions. We found that by setting each function of x equal to y (that is, $f(x) = y$) we could algebraically solve a given system of equations. We were most interested in *independent and consistent systems* and found that a unique solution existed whenever the number of independent equations at our command was equal to the number of variables in the equations. Factoring skills, knowledge of slope, graphing, and the application of the properties of the real number system enabled us to solve most systems in two or more different ways.

We learned how to graph linear inequalities by sketching closed and open half-planes. We graphed solutions for systems of linear inequalities and applied these skills in the solution of linear programing problems — problems that on first appearance seemed impossible to solve, but when graphed, became easy. We recalled that a major danger in working with inequalities is the reversal of the inequality sign when multiplying both sides of an inequality by a negative number.

Once again, we found a need for some number outside the set of real numbers when we tried to evaluate a solution of $x = \sqrt{-5}$ or $x^2 = -5$. Since this result was obtained in our attempt to find the intersection of a quadratic equation and a linear equation, some meaningful identification of this intersection was naturally demanded, just as we sought closure when we obtained the meaningless situation of $x + 7 = 3$ in set C.

The underlying purpose of this entire chapter was to bring into perspective the integrative power of algebra by focusing on a given problem the many ideas and skills known by you thus far. The need for the ideas and skills you have learned in grade one through high school and college should have become apparent. With a little reflection, you should now be able to see and appreciate the "forest of algebra and not have your view obstructed by the trees." Your wider view should not detract from the appeal of an individual tree, but should encourage closer examination of several of the trees.

Just as many problems involving fractions are impossible to a fourth grader but easily solved by an eighth grader who has studied the rational numbers, so should you now be able to see many problems that can be easily solved although they formerly appeared improbable if not impossible. It should now be clear to you that algebra is a *generalization* of arithmetic. The value of a generalized statement such as the quadratic formula compared to factoring by "reasoned inspection" should be clear.

Your knowledge and understanding should now permit you to answer in a positive manner the fifth grade student who some day may wonder about the sum of consecutive integers:

"Teacher, isn't there some way we can tell how much these add up to no matter what number we stop at?"

This pupil is seeking a generalization. He is on the verge of breaking into algebraic thought on his own. He should be encouraged to experiment with his idea. Try it yourself. Experiment with the following sums:

$$1 + 2 + 3 + 4 + 5 + 6 = 21 \tag{1}$$
$$1 + 2 + 3 + 4 + 5 + 6 + 7 = 28 \tag{2}$$
$$1 + 2 + 3 + \cdots + 12 + 13 = 91 \tag{3}$$
$$1 + 2 + 3 + \cdots + 13 + 14 = 105 \tag{4}$$

How much does $1 + 2 + 3 + \cdots + n$ equal? That is the penetrating question posed by the fifth grader! If he comes up with the statement "when n is an even number, the answer is always $\frac{1}{2}n \cdot (n+1)$," your answer should be:

"Johnny, that's correct and it's brilliant! Can you figure out what it will be if n is odd?"

Can you figure out what the sum will be whether n is odd *or* even? Can you *prove* your theorem? (No checking your answer on page z this time. If you get it right, you will *know* it!)

CHAPTER REVIEW TEST

1. If y equals a second-degree polynomial in x, how many times does the graph of the equation intersect the y axis? The x axis? Explain both answers.

2. In problem 1, if x and y are variables in R, which of the variables is a function of the other?

3. If a function F is defined as $F(y) = x$, what can be said immediately regarding the graph of this function?

Solve and graph the following systems:

4. $\begin{cases} x = y - 3 \\ 2x + y = 0 \end{cases}$
   5. $\begin{cases} x - 2y = 3 \\ 4y + 2x = 6 \end{cases}$

6. The sum of two numbers is 77. The first number added to twice the second makes 114. Find the two numbers algebraically.

7. If 27 is subtracted from a two-digit number the digits will be reversed. The sum of the digits of the number is 9. Find the original number.

8. If 3 pounds of bacon and 2 pounds of butter cost $3.20 and 2 pounds of bacon and 5 pounds of butter cost $3.60, what is the price of bacon and butter per pound?

9. The sum of the digits in a three-digit number is 12. The sum of the first and second digits is 4 less than the third. When 693 is added to the number, the digits are reversed. Find the number.

Solve the following independent system of equations:

10. $\begin{cases} 2x + y = z + 1 \\ x - y - z = 2 \\ x - z = 1 \end{cases}$
    11. $\begin{cases} 2x - y + 2z = 1 \\ x - z = y - 3 \\ z + x = y \end{cases}$
    12. $\begin{cases} x + y + z = 1 \\ x = y + 2 \\ y - z = 1 \end{cases}$

Graph each of the following systems of inequalities and then tabulate the solution set of ordered pairs (x, y) such that x and y are elements of I for the given three constraints:

13. $\begin{cases} 2x \geq y \\ x + y < 5 \\ y > -2 \end{cases}$
    14. $\begin{cases} y \leq 2 \\ 2x + y > 2 \\ x - y < 1 \end{cases}$

Complete in your own words:

15. A function is . . .
16. Algebra is . . .
17. A point in the Cartesian coordinate system lies above the line $ay = mx + k$ if and only if . . .

18. The function game (as defined on page 125) might profitably be played for what purpose in grade 1? In grade 3? In grade 6?

19. Derive a formula for finding the value of:

$$1 - 2 + 3 - 4 + 5 - 6 + 7 - \cdots n$$

if n is even; if n is odd.

20. Derive a formula for finding the sum of

$$1^2 + 2^2 + 3^2 + 4^2 + \cdots + n^2$$

If you fail to find the sum, discover where you can look up such things in any good library. Can you find it in a standard encyclopedia?

CHECKING YOUR WORK

page 125

1. Sample answers:

$$G(0) = 2 \cdot 0 - 7 \cdot 0 - 3 = -3$$
$$G(1) = 2 \cdot 1 - 7 \cdot 1 - 3 = 2 - 10 = -8$$

2. One possible answer:

$$f(x) = x - 1$$

because

$$f(2) = 1, \quad f(4) = 3, \quad \text{and} \quad f(6) = 5$$

Is $f(x) = 1$ another possible answer? Yes, because $f(x) = 1 + 0x$.

3. The domain is the set of points on the globe. The range is the set of numbers representing altitude.

4. $h(0) = 2$
$$h(-3) = (-3)^2 - (-3) + 2 = 14$$
$$h(\tfrac{1}{2}) = (\tfrac{1}{2})^2 - \tfrac{1}{2} + 2 = \tfrac{1}{4} - \tfrac{1}{2} + 2 = 1\tfrac{3}{4}$$

5. The domain is the set of people. The range is the set of seats. The relation — for each person there is one seat.

6. The domain is the number of correct answers. The range is the set of grades.
Rule — the number of correct answers determines the grade.

7. At least one vertical line can be drawn that intersects the graph in two points. Yes, it represents a function of y.

In summary, we can say that each element in the domain of a function is paired with one and only one element of the range, and not all elements of the range need be used.

Return to page 125

page 137

Figure 4-15 shows two more types of solution sets—the null set and a single point set. The null set is the solution set of the parabola and the line l_3. The equation for the parabola is $x^2 = y$. The equation for l_3 is $y = -5$. The graph makes the null set intersection obvious, but what do we find if we proceed algebraically—another inconsistent result?

Figure 4-15

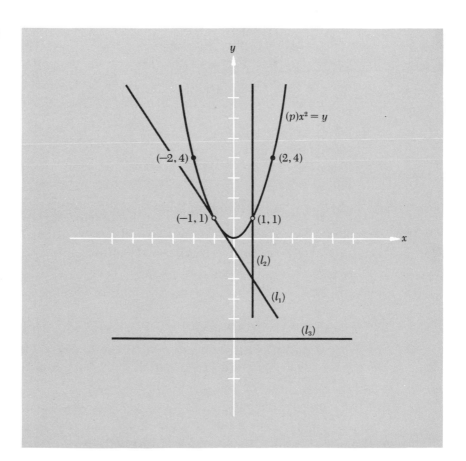

Substituting the value of $y = -5$ in the equation of the parabola, we find $x^2 = -5$. However, we have no element in the real numbers that when squared equals a negative integer, because we know that for all a in R, $a \cdot a \geqq 0$. Recall that we ended with the false equation $0 = -5$ when we algebraically solved an inconsistent system of linear equations. Our result here of $x^2 = -5$ is an open statement for which we may try to find a value of x to make the statement true, but to test its truth would entail an extension of the real numbers to obtain closure under the square root operation. We should remember that the statement $8 - x = 15$ in the universe of C was "unworkable"; that is, no solution existed within C. This did not mean the condition was necessarily impossible to satisfy. The condition *was* indeed possible to satisfy when we expanded to a universe of the set I. So, too, $x^2 = -5$ is "unworkable" in the universe R, but perhaps if we expanded our universe . . . ? Obviously we must do just this if we are to obtain closure under the operation of taking the square root of a real number. This need for expansion becomes more demanding as we progress, but for now let it suffice to say that our result $x^2 = -5$ indicates there is no solution point in the universe of real numbers for this system. The solution set then is $\varnothing$.

Turn now to the systems graphed in Figure 4-15, which have only one solution point. There are four such possible nonlinear systems.

1. The parabola and the y axis $(x = 0)$.
2. The parabola and l_2.
3. The parabola and the x axis $(y = 0)$.
4. The parabola and l_1.

Let us discuss these four possibilities. We say that for any parabola symmetric about the y axis, any line parallel to the y axis (including the y axis itself) intersects the parabola at only one point. (Using Figure 4-15, how would you support this statement if the line in question were $x = 182$?) This first statement takes care of possibilities 1 and 2.

For possibility 3, we say for any parabola of the general form $ax^2 = y + k$ ($a \neq 0$, and $a, k \in R$), a line parallel to the x axis passing through the vertex of the parabola intersects the parabola at only that one point.

Finally, for possibility 4, such a parabola and any line that is tangent to the parabola intersect only at the one point of tangency. (Note that possibility 3 is simply a special case of possibility 4.)

Do you see the relation between the definition of a function and the necessity for the qualification imposed in the discussion of possibilities 1 and 2? Only because y is a *function* of x do we know possibilities 1 and 2 intersect at only one point. You can clarify this concept for yourself by supposing the parabola had *not* been a function — suppose instead of a parabola we had had $x^2 + y^2 = 25$, a circle. In such a case, *two* values of y correspond to any value of x; similarly, two values of x correspond to any value of y.

Return to page 137

page
144

The shaded area in Figure 4-16 together with the line compose the solution set to the condition $x - y \leq 0$. It is obvious from the graph that the point (4, 0) does *not* satisfy the condition. Furthermore, by direct substitution in the condition, we find $4 - 0 = 4 \nleq 0$.

**Figure
4-16**

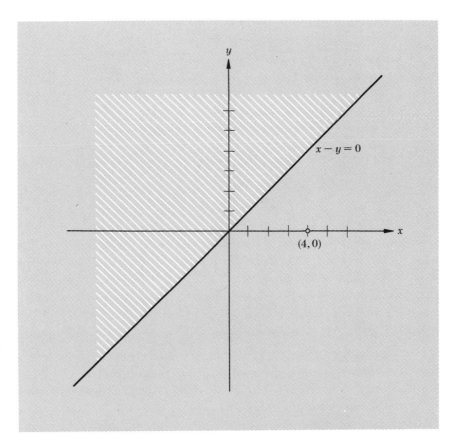

$x - y = 0$

(4, 0)

Here then is a condition involving "is less than" for which the solution set consists of all the points above the line, not below it! What is the difference between this condition and all those with which we have previously worked? Address yourself to this question if you have not already answered it satisfactorily. (Do not read further— close your book and think—or look back and determine what all the previous conditions had in common that differs from our condition here.)

Before confirming your finding, let us first gather the knowledge we need and then apply it to the problem. We should recall, for example, that we do not rewrite inequalities or work with them exactly as we do equations, because the usual cancellation law of multiplication does not hold for an inequality in R. For example, if we multiply both sides of an obvious inequality by a negative integer, we arrive at a false statement: $3 < 4$ so $-2 \cdot 3 < -2 \cdot 4$ and $-6 < -8$. This is false because $-6 \not< -8$. Thus, we find that if we multiply both sides of an inequality by a negative number, we reverse the relation!

Secondly, we recall there are some advantages in rewriting linear equations in the standard slope form of $y = mx + k$, which we can, in turn, view as a function of x, namely, $f(x) = mx + k$. Now perhaps you found that all conditions with which we have worked previously have a positive coefficient of y, whereas in the inequality $x - y \leq 0$ the coefficient of y is negative. We know from our review that if we multiply both sides of this condition by -1, we reverse the inequality and obtain $y - x \geq 0$. Intuitively, we begin to see that *if and only if* the coefficient of y is positive can we state that any point above the line satisfies the condition "is greater than" and any point below the line satisfies "is less than."

We can treat the inequality as an equation and solve for y, and consider the right-hand side as a function, say $f(x)$. For the condition in question, we find $f(x) = x$ and obtain the graph of the line in Figure 4-16. Furthermore, to satisfy the relation of $y > x$, there must be a real number $k > 0$ such that $y = x + k$; in all such cases, y must be above any given point on the line. We can thus state:

The solution set for $y < mx + k$ is the set of all points lying below the line representing $y = mx + k$, and the set of all points lying above this line is the solution set for $y > mx + k$.

Return to page 144

page
148
At point (5, 5) the profit would be $1500.00. At (4, 4) it would be $1200.00. At (5, 6) it would be $1600.00; but, of course, this is impossible. Why? Because the third restraint of a 10,000 barrel maximum production per day makes the production of 11,000 barrels a day impossible.

No, point (7, 3) is not in the polygon because of the fourth restraint limiting the number of barrel-miles the trucks can provide. The delivery of 7000 barrels of gasoline and 3000 barrels of jet fuel would demand 270,000 barrel-miles per day, which exceeds the allowable maximum of 210,000 barrel-miles.

Return to page 148

5

COMPLEX NUMBERS

Do you recall our frustration when we were working with the set of counting numbers and tried to find a solution for an equation such as $3 + x = 1$? Expansion of the set of counting numbers to the set of integers enabled us to find a nonempty solution set for such an equation. Similarly, the expansion of the set I to the set Ra enabled us to find a nonempty solution set for an equation such as $2x = 3$. An expansion to the set R made possible a nonempty solution set for $x^2 = 2$.

Each expansion that we have made added a new set of numerals and a new kind of number to our view. Each expansion was very carefully developed to test whether the properties of the original set still held for the new set. That is, when the set of integers was expanded to the set of rationals, properties such as the commutative and associative properties of the two binary operations $+$ and $\cdot$ were carefully shown to hold; the distributive property was checked over the new set; the additive identity (zero) was maintained, as was the multiplicative identity (1). As a matter of fact, all the properties that we had in the set of integers were found to hold in the set Ra; moreover, a bonus property of the multiplicative inverse was obtained, which provided closure for the set under the operation division! (We require the divisor to be different from zero.)

Again when the rationals were expanded to the real numbers, all properties were carefully checked and found to be valid. With this extension the number line was finally completed—there were no "holes" left in it—each point on the number line could now be placed in a one-to-one correspondence with an element of the real number set!

5.1 The Field Properties

Looking back over the study of the real numbers, we are now in a position to see that the rational number system was the first system in which we could add, subtract, multiply, and divide (except by zero) without obtaining a number outside the set. In short, the rationals are *closed under all four operations.* Such a system is called a *field.* Because expansion of *Ra* (an ordered field) to *R* does not destroy any of the rules, properties, and laws of *Ra*, but adds the property of completeness, *R* is called a *complete ordered field.*

We now again need some new number or numbers if we are to solve every quadratic equation. If we demand a nonempty solution set for the equation $x^2 = -1$, we must obviously expand our set of symbols once more. In this case, why not just call the number you need *i*, union it with the set *R* and go merrily on your way? Why should we care whether the new set is a field or not? We do very well with the set of integers in many cases and yet it is not a field. We dealt almost exclusively with the set *C* for four years in the elementary schools, and it also is not a field. So why should we examine the new system if we expand our old system, for the field properties?

These are pertinent questions and are posed here at the beginning of this chapter in the hope that the answers to them may place the work of the rest of this chapter in better perspective.

If we can expand the set *R* in some way, the value of the new system depends a great deal on whether or not we can use it. If we cannot add, subtract, multiply, or divide with it, why would we want it?

In most measurement problems, we need only the set of nonnegative real numbers. In other areas, we need the set of integers. Because fractions are a very real part of our lives, we prefer the set *Ra* to the set *I* and consider someone who cannot work with fractions to be uneducated (a synonym for ignorant). In general, we find that the more field properties a system has, the more applications it has. Speaking more broadly, we could say that the lower the level of civilization, the fewer the field properties needed.

We add no mathematical content to a textbook, to our knowledge, or to our conversation when we add the word *field.* It is simply a word we use to refer to a particular set of ideas we already understand. However, the word *field* is easier and shorter to write and say than to continually list all the ideas it represents. It has the same very real value to us as does the word *polynomial*.

So let us agree that we will do well if, in expanding the system of real numbers, we can maintain the field properties. To help us in our work, let us review the meaning of a field.

DEFINITION 5-1 ————————————————————————————

A **field** is a set S containing at least two distinct elements and having the following properties:

1. S is closed under two binary operations so that for all $a, b \in S$ we obtain:

   $a + b \in S$ and $a \cdot b \in S$

2. The associative property holds for both operations so that for all $a, b, c \in S$ we have:

   $a + (b + c) = (a + b) + c$
   $a \cdot (b \cdot c) = (a \cdot b) \cdot c$

3. The commutative property holds for both operations so that for all $a, b \in S$ we have:

   $a + b = b + a$ and $a \cdot b = b \cdot a$

4. Identity elements, denoted by 0 and 1, exist such that for all $a \in S$:

   $a + 0 = a$ and $a \cdot 1 = a$

5. Inverse elements exist such that for all $a \in S$:

   $a + (-a) = 0$ and $a \cdot (a^{-1}) = 1 \quad (a \neq 0)$

6. The distributive property holds in that $\cdot$ distributes over $+$ for all $a, b, c \in S$,

   $a \cdot (b + c) = (a \cdot b) + (a \cdot c)$

——

EXERCISES
5.1

Consider the set C and the operations $+$ and $\cdot$ (that is, addition and multiplication).

1. Is C closed under the two operations?
2. Does the associative property hold for both operations?
3. Does the commutative property hold for both operations?
4. Does a multiplicative identity exist?
5. Does an additive identity exist?
6. Do inverse elements exist?
7. Does multiplication distribute over addition?
8. Why is C not a field?
9. Why is I not a field?

5.2 The Number i

We are now ready to attack the problem of finding a nonempty solution set for the equation $x^2 = -1$ by expanding the real number system. Since we are familiar with the operations $+$ and $\cdot$ and have practice in their use, it would be most advantageous if we could accomplish the expansion and keep intact the symbols, operations, and properties as we have known them in the real number system. Ideally, we would like to obtain a new system having all the properties of the real number system and providing a solution set to any quadratic equation.

Let us begin by letting i be an abbreviation for $\sqrt{-1}$. That is, we arbitrarily pick the symbol i to represent the number $\sqrt{-1}$. This definition is in accord with long established tradition. Presumably i is the abbreviation for the word *imaginary*, the term used to name the numbers we want to add. It was logical to reason that since $\sqrt{-1}$ is not a real number, it must be imaginary; hence, the term and the symbol. But just as the "unutterable" $\sqrt{2}$ is a very real and useful number, so, too, the number i was found to be useful—and hardly imaginary! Its most common practical application lies in the field of electrical engineering, which is commonly considered a utilitarian area of endeavor.

What do we know about our new number i? We know that i is the name we have given a solution of the equation $x^2 = -1$. By definition, then, we know that $i^2 = -1$. This is the one relation we have between our new number and the set of real numbers. We must build and capitalize on this one relation, just as we did in expanding the set W to include the negative integers. In that case, all we knew was that we agreed to call the additive inverse of a "negative a." That is, we knew $a + (-a) = 0$. Proceeding from this relation, we found the set I

was closed under the operation of addition, multiplication, and sub-traction. We found that the commutative and associative properties of multiplication and addition held. We found the distributive property to be still valid. We found each element of *I* had an additive inverse, and we observed that zero acted as an additive inverse. In short, we found the integers had all of the properties of a field except that of the multiplicative inverse. We call such a set a *ring*. Further-more, because multiplication is commutative, we call the set of integers a *commutative ring* with identity. In simpler terms, the integers form a set that is closed under the three operations of addi-tion, subtraction, and multiplication.

Well, what then can we discover regarding the expanded set of real numbers and *i*? That is, what can be determined regarding the set $R \cup \{i\}$? Since we want our definitions and operations in the expanded set to be the same as those for the set of real numbers, we note that

$$\sqrt{-1} \cdot \sqrt{-1} = (\sqrt{-1})^2 = -1 = i^2$$

Hence,

$$(\sqrt{-1})^2 = i^2$$

and

$$\sqrt{-1} = i$$

which is our original definition.

We wish to construct a new field containing the set *R* and the element *i* and at the same time to retain the integrity of the subfield *R*. Hence we wish to use, if possible, the set $R \cup \{i\}$ and the two binary operations of addition and multiplication to obtain the new field.

Property 4 of a field (see page 161) states that identity elements must exist in the set. Since we wish to retain the integrity of the sub-field *R*, we see that the following relations must also exist:

$$i + 0 = i \qquad \text{and} \qquad i \cdot 1 = i$$

Property 5 of a field demands the existence of inverse elements, thus

$$i + (-i) = 0, \qquad i \cdot i^{-1} = 1, \qquad \text{and} \qquad \frac{i}{i} = 1$$

The alert student may notice that $i \cdot (-i) = 1$, because

$$i \cdot (-i) = -(i \cdot i) = -(i^2) = -(-1) = 1$$

But since $i \cdot (-i) = 1$, is not $-i$ then the multiplicative inverse of *i*?

Or is it i^{-1}? Can we have *two* multiplicative inverses of i? Are i^{-1} and $-i$ just different names for the same number? Can they be equal? Consider this question and discover for yourself that they are, indeed, equal.

The interesting fact we have just discovered is that $-i$ is *both* the additive and multiplicative inverse of i, thus,

$$i + (-i) = 0 \qquad \text{and} \qquad i \cdot (-i) = 1$$

Let us summarize what we have accepted or discovered regarding i.

1. $-1 = i^2$	(definition)
2. $i + 0 = i$	(field property 4)
3. $i \cdot 1 = i$	(field property 4)
4. $i + (-i) = 0$	(field property 5)
5. $i \cdot i^{-1} = 1$ (or $i \cdot (-i) = 1$)	(field property 5)
6. $i^{-1} = -i$	

EXERCISES
5.2

Simplify the following problems:

1. i^2
2. i^4
3. $i^3 - i$
4. $(i^2)^3$

5. $(i^4)(i^2)$
6. $i^4 - i^2$
7. $i(i^2 - i) + i^2$
8. $(1 - i)/[i(i^3 - i)]$

9. Show that $-i = i^{-1}$

5.3   The Set $R \cup \{i\}$

In view of our summary statements regarding i, let us examine field property 1, which demands that $R \cup \{i\}$ must be closed under the operations of addition and multiplication. Consider first the demand for addition. Our new set is the union of R and $\{i\}$. Therefore, we must obtain either an element of R or the element i when we add i and any element of R.

Consider, for example, $a \in R$ and the result $a + i$. If we have closure, this sum must yield either an element of R or i itself. Let us assume the former:

$a + i = b$ where $a, b \in R$

then

$(-a) + a + i = (-a) + b$ (adding $-a$ to each side)

and

$i = (-a) + b$

But this is a contradiction, since $i \notin R$ and $(-a+b) \in R$! Our assumption that $a + i$ is an element of R must be false. Hence, we consider the other possibility. Assume

$a + i = i$

Adding $-i$ to each side, we have

$a + i + (-i) = i + (-i)$

or

$a = 0$

Thus if $a \neq 0$, we again arrive at a contradiction.

Does this mean we have reached an impasse? Since the sum of $a + i$ yields neither an element of R nor the element i (if $a \neq 0$), are we through with our attempt to find a new field using the set $R \cup \{i\}$? Can we find another solution to our attempt to find a new field, called perhaps $C^\#$, with R as a subfield? Think about the answer to this question before reading further.

When developing ideas in the field of R, it is often helpful to "see what happens" in an ordinary arithmetic example. Let us follow this practice here. What would happen if we had to find the sum

$6 + i + (-4) + i + 2 + i + (-i) + -2 + i + i$

Since we are seeking to construct a field, we will assume that the associative and commutative properties hold, associate all elements of R, and note their sum to be $6 + -4 + 2 + -2 = 2$. Associating the i's, we find the sum $i + i + i + (-i) + i + i$. Adding these values as we would in the set of integers we say this sum is $4i$. Thus the original example would simplify to $2 + 4i$. Intuitively we feel that any sum of elements of R and i can be reduced to a number of the type $a + bi$ where $a, b \in R$. (Can you demonstrate the correctness of our intuition by applying the distributive law?)

Perhaps we were shortsighted when we tried to expand R to only the union of R and $\{i\}$. Maybe we should have expanded to a new set of numbers that take the form of $a + bi$, where $a, b \in R$.

1. Would such a set contain R as a subset?

2. Would it contain $\{i\}$ as a subset?

3. How would we add two numbers of the form $a + bi$?

4. Would *this* set be closed under addition?

Do your best to answer these four questions on your own and then

CHECK YOUR WORK on page 189

5.4 The Complex Numbers

Now let us simplify the notation for our set of symbols. We call our new set the set $C^\#$, and let the symbols represent what we call *complex numbers*. We formally define the set of complex numbers as the set

$$C^\# = \{a + bi \mid a, b \in R \text{ and } i = \sqrt{-1}\}$$

We understand that if $c, d, k,$ and m are elements of R, then $c + di$ and $k + mi$ are elements of $C^\#$.

We now have a set $C^\#$, which we have found to be closed under the operation addition. We also want closure under multiplication. Do we have it? Does $(a + bi) \cdot (c + di) = (k + mi)$? Let us try to prove that it does.

$(a + bi)(c + di)$
$\quad = (a + bi)c + (a + bi)di \qquad$ (distributive property)
$\quad = ac + bic + adi + bidi \qquad$ (distributive property)
$\quad = ac + bci + adi + bdi^2 \qquad$ (commutative property)
$\quad = ac + bci + adi + bd(-1) \qquad$ (definition of i^2)
$\quad = ac - bd + bci + adi \qquad$ (commutative property)
$\quad = (ac - bd) + (bci + adi) \qquad$ (associative property)
$\quad = (ac - bd) + (bc + ad)i \qquad$ (distributive property)
$\quad = k + mi \qquad$ where $(ac - bd) = k, (bc + ad) = m$

Note that $k, m \in R$, since R is closed under addition, subtraction, and multiplication. Hence, the set $C^\#$ *is closed* under multiplication. In view of the above we can define multiplication as

$(a + bi)(c + di) = (ac - bd) + (bc + ad)i$

Stated in words, we could say "the product of two elements of $C^{\#}$ is a unique element of $C^{\#}$, the first term of which is the sum of the product of the first terms and the additive inverse of the product of the i coefficients; the second term is the product of i and its coefficient (where the coefficient of i is determined by the sum of the product of the i coefficient of the first number and the first term of the second number and the product of the first term of the first number and the i coefficient of the second number)."

Such a cumbersome statement is almost useless except as an exercise in exactness of English usage. To make our definition of multiplication in $C^{\#}$ more meaningful, we need to relate it to what we previously learned and did in the real number system. With closure under multiplication, we know that $(a + bi)(c + di) = k + mi$ (where $a, b, c, d, k, m \in R$). From our definition of multiplication in $C^{\#}$, we know that

$(a + bi)(c + di) = (ac - bd) + (bc + ad)i$

From these two facts we see that

$k = (ac - bd) \qquad \text{and} \qquad m = (bc + ad)$

The similarity between multiplication in $C^{\#}$ and multiplication of two binomials in R should now be evident. Recall the means and extremes rule discussed in Chapter 2. Let us define multiplication in $C^{\#}$ in these terms and see what we have.

DEFINITION 5-2 ———————————————————————

The **product of two complex numbers** $(a + bi)(c + di)$ is equal to the product of their first terms (ac) plus the sum of the products of the mean terms and the extreme terms $(bci + adi)$, plus the product of the end terms (bdi^2).

———————————————————————————————————————

This discussion is in agreement with our previous description of multiplication, because the product here obtained is

$(ac) + (bci + adi) + (bdi^2)$

which simplifies to

$(ac - bd) + (bc + ad)i$

Just as the means and extremes process of multiplying two binomials was shown to be in direct correspondence with the common multiplication algorithm used in the elementary school, multiplication of complex numbers can be shown to have the same correspondence. Rather than write all the steps of such an algorithm every time we wish to find the product of two complex numbers, we simply use the means and extremes rule for multiplying two binomials or we memorize the following rule:

$$(a + bi)(c + di) = (ac - bd) + (bc + ad)i$$

All elementary school children must memorize the basic fact that 7 times 8 is 56. Somewhere within a week to three years most of them establish the correct answer of "fifty-six" as a conditioned response. It will similarly be profitable for you if you commit the basic rules of addition and multiplication in $C^\#$ to memory before we test further to determine if $C^\#$, like R, is a complete, ordered field.

To exercise our memory and skill in applying our two definitions let us find several sums and products. To find the *sum* of $7 + 6i$ and $4 + 2i$, we write, according to our rule for addition, $(7 + 4) + (6 + 2)i$. Adding the real numbers involved, we obtain as a final sum $11 + 8i$. Adding $6 + i$ and $4 - 3i$ and omitting the intermediate step, we can write the answer immediately as $10 - 2i$.

To find the *product* of $3 + 4i$ and $2 + 3i$, we write according to our rule for multiplication $(3 \cdot 2 - 4 \cdot 3) + (4 \cdot 2 + 3 \cdot 3)i$. Again performing the indicated operations with the real numbers, we simplify this to the final answer $-6 + 17i$. Let us illustrate one more example, to multiply $6 + i$ and $4 - 3i$, omitting the intermediate step, we can write immediately $27 - 14i$.

EXERCISES
5.4

These exercises are designed to teach you the correct conditioned response. To best achieve this objective, do only enough of the problems the first day to establish an automatic procedure. Twenty-four hours later try several more, and if your response is still automatic, finish the rest of the problems two days later.

1. $(7 + 2i) + (3 + 4i)$ 5. $(4 + 7i) - (2 + 3i)$
2. $(1 + i) + (12 + i)$ 6. $(9 + 3i) - (9 + i)$
3. $(3 - 2i) + (4 + 2i)$ 7. $(2 + i) - (3 - 4i)$
4. $(5 - 6i) + (3 + 6i)$ 8. $i + (5 + 5i)$

9. $-5 + (6 - 2i)$

10. $(3 - 4i) - (1 - 4i)$

11. $(7 + 2i)(3 + 4i)$

12. $(1 + i)(12 + i)$

13. $(3 - 2i)(4 + 2i)$

14. $(5 - 6i)(3 + 6i)$

15. $(4 + 7i)(2 + 3i)$

16. $(9 + 3i)(9 + i)$

17. $(2 + i)(3 - 4i)$

18. $i(5 + 5i)$

19. $-5(6 - 2i)$

20. $(3 - 4i)(1 - 4i)$

In problems 21–26 your conditioned response should speed simplification, but for accuracy, you should use pencil and paper.

21. $-(7 - 2i)(-3 - i) + (4 - 3i)$

22. $\frac{1}{2}(4 - 10i)(1 - i) - 3i + 6 + 2i - 4i + (i - 5)$

23. $(3 + 2i)(4i - 6)$

24. $(4i - 6)(2i + 3)$

25. $-\frac{1}{4}(2i + 4)(2i - 4) + (2i + 4)^2$

26. $(2i + 3)(2i - 3) - 15i^2$

5.5 Addition and Multiplication in the Complex Numbers

Did it occur to you while doing the preceding exercises that you could treat the number i as you formerly treated a variable in an equation? That is, problem 26 can be considered as though the problem were

$(2X + 3)(2X - 3) - 15X^2$
$= 4X^2 - 9 - 15X^2$
$= -11X^2 - 9$

Since $X^2 = i^2 = -1$, the binomial becomes

$-11(-1) - 9$

or

$11 - 9 = 2$

In problem 24 of Exercises 5.4 did you notice that the answer you wrote as a conditioned response could also have been obtained by viewing the problem as you did the multiplication of two binomials? That is,

$(4i - 6)(2i + 3) = 8i^2 + (-12i + 12i) - 18$
$= 8i^2 - 18 = 8(-1) - 18$
$= -8 - 18 = -26$

If you proceeded in this manner in solving some of the exercises, you are to be commended! You will remember to multiply out and collect terms (remembering that $i^2 = -1$) long after you have forgotten the memorized rule.

Let us examine this idea more closely. You were first asked to memorize a rule for multiplying. You were directed to exercise the application of this rule until it became a conditioned response. Then a method of multiplying in $C^\#$ was discussed, which is easier to understand and represents a more nearly *permanent* learning. This concept of more nearly permanent learning is a fundamental tenet in the argument for *understanding* as a goal in elementary school mathematics rather than only memorization and rote application of rules.

EXERCISES
5.5

Simplify the following problems.

1. $(2 + i)i + 3i$
2. $(3 + 2i)(2 + i)$
3. $(1 - i)(1 + i)$
4. $(1 - i)^2$
5. $(6 + 2i)(2 + 7i)$
6. $(i^2 + 2i + 1)/i^2$
7. $(1 + i^2)(2 + i)(i - 4)$
8. $(4 - 2i)(3 - 3i)$
9. $(2 - i)(2 + i)$
10. $(5 + 5i)(2 - 2i)$

5.6 The Complex Numbers as a Field

Let us review how far we have progressed toward our stated goal of expanding the real number system to the complex number system. We have established that

$$C^\# = \{(a + bi)|a, b \in R, i = \sqrt{-1}\}$$

and that $C^\#$ is closed under addition and multiplication. Thus we have a set and the first field property. Let us examine the field property of associativity.

Field Property 2 – Associativity [1]

We must show that

$$[(a + bi) + (c + di)] + (e + fi) = (a + bi) + [(c + di) + (e + fi)]$$

---

[1] See page 161.

By applying the rule for addition in $C^\#$ to both sides of the equation we obtain

$$[(a + c) + (b + d)i] + (e + fi) = (a + bi) + [(c + e) + (d + f)i]$$
$$(a + c + e) + (b + d + f)i = (a + c + e) + (b + d + f)i$$

We find by inspection that these two numbers are the same; thus, the associative property of addition holds.

Show that the associative property of multiplication also holds and then

CHECK YOUR WORK on page 190

Field Property 3 – Commutativity [2]

If the commutative property of addition is to hold, we must show that

$$(a + bi) + (c + di) = (c + di) + (a + bi)$$

Applying the rule for addition to both sides, we have

$$(a + c) + (b + d)i = (c + a) + (d + b)i$$
$$\qquad\qquad\quad = (a + c) + (b + d)i \qquad \text{(commutative property}$$
$$\text{of addition in } R)$$

Establishing the commutative property of multiplication for $C^\#$ is left to you as an exercise.

Field Property 4a – Additive Identity [3]

Is it true that

$$(a + bi) + (0 + 0i) = a + bi$$

Performing the addition on the left, we obtain $(a + 0) + (b + 0)i$. Applying property four of the real number system, we obtain $a + bi$. Is this sufficient to establish the additive identity? Can you show that $(a + bi) + 0 = a + bi$? How can this be used to show that $(0 + 0i) = 0$?

Field Property 4b – Multiplicative Identity

We must show that

$$(a + bi) \cdot 1 = a + bi$$

---

[2] See page 161.
[3] See page 161.

for all $a, b \in R$ and a, b not both zero. Let us find values for $x, y \in R$ such that $(a + bi)(x + yi) = (a + bi)$; that is, we seek a complex number $(x + yi)$ that equals our old friend 1. If $x + yi$ is to equal 1, then obviously $x = 1$ and $y = 0$. Testing this, we find

$$(a + bi)(1 + 0i) = (a \cdot 1 - b \cdot 0) + (b \cdot 1 + a \cdot 0)i$$
$$= a + bi$$

Field Property 5a – Additive Inverse [4]

Does there exist an element $(c + di)$ such that

$$(a + bi) + (c + di) = 0$$

By addition, we find $(a + c) + (b + d)i = 0$. Hence, if $c = -a$ and $d = -b$, then $[(a + (-a)] + [(b + (-b)]i = 0 + 0i = 0$. Substituting these values for c and d in our original equation, we now find $(a + bi) + [(-a) + (-bi)] = 0$, and $[(-a) + (-bi)]$ is seen to be the additive inverse of $(a + bi)$.

Field Property 5b – Multiplicative Inverse

Is there an element $(c + di)$ such that

$$(a + bi)(c + di) = 1$$

By now you should have grasped the general procedures followed in developing suitable answers to questions like this. How can we proceed to show there is a multiplicative inverse, and how can we find what it is for a given number $a + bi$? Given the following general directions and hints, you should be able to find the values of c and d.

Assume that $c + di$ is the multiplicative inverse of $a + bi$. Use the rule for multiplication to multiply $a + bi$ and $c + di$. By applying the properties of $C^\#$, develop a system of simultaneous equations in R to determine the values of c and d. Allow yourself enough time and when you are sure of your answer,

CHECK YOUR WORK on page 190

Field Property 6 – Distributivity

We need to show that

$$(a + bi)[(c + di) + (e + fi)] = (a + bi)(c + di) + (a + bi)(e + fi)$$

---

[4] See page 161.

First, we compute the left side of the equation.

$(a + bi)[(c + di) + (e + fi)]$

$\quad = (a + bi)[(c + e) + (d + f)i]$ (adding)

$\quad = [a(c + e) - b(d + f)] + [b(c + e) + a(d + f)]i$ (multiplying)

$\quad = (ac + ae - bd - bf) + (bc + be + ad + af)i$ (field properties of R)

We have shown that the left side equals the unique element of $C^{\#}$ shown in the last step. We now compute the right side in the hope that it also equals the same complex number.

$(a + bi)(c + di) + (a + bi)(e + fi)$

$\quad = [(ac - bd) + (bc + ad)i] + [(ae - bf) + (be + af)i]$

$\qquad\qquad\qquad\qquad\qquad$ (multiplying)

$\quad = (ac - bd + ae - bf) + [(bc + ad)i + (be + af)i]$

$\qquad\qquad\qquad\qquad\qquad$ (adding complex numbers)

$\quad = (ac + ae - bd - bf) + (bc + be + ad + af)i$

$\qquad\qquad\qquad\qquad\qquad$ (commuting)

We have completed both sides and found them to be equal to the same complex number! Because of the transitive property of equals, we conclude that multiplication is distributive over addition in our new set $C^{\#}$.

Let us summarize our results for $C^{\#}$.

DEFINITION 5-3 —————————————————————————————

The field of complex numbers consists of:

1. The set of complex numbers:

   $\{a + bi \,|\, a, b \in R \text{ and } i = \sqrt{-1}\}$

2. The operation $(+)$ defined as:

   $(a + bi) + (c + di) = (a + c) + (b + d)i$

3. The operation $(\cdot)$ defined as:

   $(a + bi)(c + di) = (ac - bd) + (bc + ad)i$

The properties of $C^{\#}$ are the following:

1. $C^{\#}$ is closed under the two binary operations addition $(+)$ and multiplication $(\cdot)$.

2. The associative property holds for both operations, that is, for all elements of $C^\#$

$$(a + bi) + [(c + di) + (e + fi)] = [(a + bi) + (c + di)] + (e + fi)$$

$$(a + bi) \cdot [(c + di) \cdot (e + fi)] = [(a + bi) \cdot (c + di)] \cdot (e + fi)$$

3. The commutative property holds for both operations; namely,

$$(a + bi) + (c + di) = (c + di) + (a + bi)$$

$$(a + bi) \cdot (c + di) = (c + di) \cdot (a + bi)$$

4. Identity elements, denoted by 0 and 1, exist such that

    a. $(c + di) + 0 = (c + di) + (0 + 0i) = (c + di)$
    b. $(c + di) \cdot 1 = (c + di)(1 + 0i) = (c + di)$

5. Inverse elements exist such that

    a. $(a + bi) + [(-a) + (-bi)] = 0$

    b. $(a + bi)\left[\left(\dfrac{a}{a^2 + b^2}\right) + \left(\dfrac{-b}{a^2 + b^2}\right)i\right] = 1, \quad \text{if } (a^2 + b^2) \neq 0$

6. The distributive property holds in that $(\cdot)$ distributes over $(+)$,

$$(a + bi)[(c + di) + (e + fi)]$$
$$= (a + bi)(c + di) + (a + bi)(e + fi)$$

5.7   The Multiplicative Inverse

Now that we have developed $C^\#$ as a field, can we use it to solve any quadratic? Can we plot numbers such as $a + bi$ on a graph as we did the elements of R? Since $C^\#$ is a field, can we define operations of subtraction and division in $C^\#$? To help us answer these questions, let us look more closely at the multiplicative inverse. Recall from the checking your work section on page 191 that the multiplicative inverse of $a + bi$ is

$$(a + bi)^{-1} = \left(\frac{a}{a^2 + b^2}\right) + \left(\frac{-b}{a^2 + b^2}\right)i \qquad (a^2 + b^2) \neq 0$$

Why did we exclude $a^2 + b^2 = 0$? How could $a^2 + b^2 = 0$ when both a and b are elements of R? *Any* nonzero element in R, when squared, yields a positive element of R. So we are really saying that a and b cannot *both* be 0. That is, we have a multiplicative inverse for all elements in $C^\#$ except $(0 + 0i)$. It follows, therefore, that we cannot divide by 0 in $C^\#$ just as we cannot divide by 0 in R. But what *is* division in $C^\#$?

Just as in R, where the product of the divisor and the quotient is the dividend, in $C^\#$ we have

$$(a + bi) \div (c + di) = (e + fi) \Longleftrightarrow (c + di)(e + fi) = (a + bi)$$

This definition is developed from

$$(c + di)(e + fi) = (a + bi)$$

If we assume that $e + fi$ is the unknown for which we wish to solve, we multiply both sides of the equation by the reciprocal of $c + di$.

$$(c + di)^{-1} \cdot (c + di) \cdot (e + fi) = (c + di)^{-1} \cdot (a + bi)$$

or

$$e + fi = \frac{a + bi}{c + di}$$

In the above discussion we assumed that 1 is always the result of multiplying a complex number by its multiplicative inverse. Let us check our assumption. If we multiply

$$(c + di) \cdot \left[\left(\frac{c}{c^2 + d^2} \right) + \left(\frac{-d}{c^2 + d^2} \right) i \right]$$

will our result be 1?

Distributing $c + di$, we find

$$\frac{(c + di)c}{c^2 + d^2} + \frac{(c + di)(-di)}{c^2 + d^2}$$

$$= \frac{c^2 + cdi}{c^2 + d^2} + \frac{-cdi - d^2i^2}{c^2 + d^2} \qquad \text{(distributive property)}$$

$$= \frac{c^2 + cdi - cdi - d^2(-1)}{c^2 + d^2} \qquad \text{(common denominator,}$$
$$\text{definition of } i^2)$$

$$= \frac{c^2 + (cdi - cdi) + d^2}{c^2 + d^2} = \frac{c^2 + d^2}{c^2 + d^2} = 1$$

Having thus verified our definition for division in $C^\#$, let us restate it as follows:

$$\frac{a + bi}{c + di} = e + fi \text{ if and only if } (a + bi) = (e + fi)(c + di)$$

Likewise, subtraction is defined in $C^\#$ as it was in I:

$$(a + bi) - (c + di) = (e + fi) \text{ if and only if } (a + bi) = (e + fi) + (c + di)$$

A more practical description of subtraction in $C^\#$ can be obtained by distributing -1 over $(c + di)$ and associating like terms. Thus

$$(a + bi) - (c + di) = (a + bi) + (-c - di)$$
$$= (a - c) + (b - d)i$$

We have now shown that $C^\#$ is a field. In short, we have shown it to be a set of elements that is closed under the operations of addition, subtraction, multiplication, and division (the divisor not zero). Before pursuing our quest for solutions to *any* quadratic, let us exercise our skills in using the four fundamental operations in $C^\#$.

EXERCISES
5.7

Reduce the following expressions to a complex number in the standard form of $a + bi$.

1. $\dfrac{2 + 3i}{3 - 2i}$

4. $\dfrac{(4 - 2i) - (3 - 2i)}{(1 - 3i)(1 + 3i)}$

2. $\dfrac{(4 + 5i) - (3 + i)}{2 + i}$

5. $\dfrac{(x + 2i)(2 - i)}{3 + i} = 1$,   solve for x

3. $\dfrac{i + 2(1 - i)}{i}$

6. $(6 + 2i)x = 6 + \sqrt{12 - 16}$,   find x

5.8 Complex Numbers as Roots of Quadratic Equations

Since we have expanded our system from R to $C^\#$ and have acquired some skill in manipulation in the universe $C^\#$, can we now solve *any* quadratic as we set out to do? Of course, in $C^\#$ the solution set to the equation $x^2 + 1 = 0$ is now seen to be $x = i$ or $x = -i$, because $i^2 + 1$ does equal 0 and $(-i)^2 + 1 = 0$. But consider an equation such as

$$x^2 - 2x + 5 = 0 \tag{1}$$

We fail to find a common factor or any special factors, and we also fail in our attempts to factor this equation by inspection. Applying the quadratic formula, we obtain

$$x = \frac{2 \pm \sqrt{4 - (4 \cdot 1 \cdot 5)}}{2} = 1 \pm \frac{\sqrt{4 - 20}}{2}$$

$$= 1 \pm \frac{\sqrt{-16}}{2} = 1 \pm \frac{\sqrt{16} \cdot \sqrt{-1}}{2} = 1 \pm \frac{4i}{2} = 1 \pm 2i$$

We note that the solution set contains the two complex numbers $1 + 2i$ and $1 - 2i$. You should check at least one of these solutions by direct substitution into equation (1).

When we examine the quadratic formula more closely than we did in Chapter 3, we note that whenever $b^2 - 4ac$ is a negative number we are dealing with the square root of a negative number; hence our solution set does not consist of real numbers, but rather, complex numbers. Looking even closer, we see that regardless of the sign and value of b, b^2 is nonnegative. Under what conditions then is the value of $b^2 - 4ac$ negative? That is, when is $b^2 - 4ac < 0$? Only when $4ac > b^2$. This expression $b^2 - 4ac$ has a special name; it is called the *discriminant* of the quadratic equation $ax^2 + bx + c = 0$. Whether the roots of a quadratic equation are real numbers or complex numbers can be determined by examining the discriminant.

Examine equation (1) again. The discriminant is seen to be

$$(-2)^2 - (4 \cdot 1 \cdot 5) = 4 - 20 = -16$$

Therefore, we know the roots are complex numbers, because the discriminant is negative.

EXERCISES
5.8

Before solving each equation below for x, determine whether its roots will be real or complex.

1. $x^2 - x + 1 = 0$
2. $x^2 + x + 1 = 0$
3. $x^2 - x - 1 = 0$
4. $-2x^2 + 5x + 63 = 0$
5. $-2x^2 + 3x = 1$
6. $2x - x^2 - 3 + 2x^2 = 2x - 4$
7. $x^2 - x + 3x = 2x^2 + x$
8. $x^2 - 12i^2 - 3x = 9 + 3xi^2 + 12$
9. $4x^2 - 12x + 8 = i^2(x^2 - 3)^0$
10. $x^2c + 2c + 3x^2 + 6 = c + 3$

5.9   Graphing Complex Numbers

Graphing was very helpful to us in working with linear and quadratic equations. As a matter of fact, we found that some quadratics had no real roots as graphically portrayed on page 75 for equations (2) and (9). When we graphed the function $y = x^2 + 4$, where $x \in R$, we found the parabola had no x intercept; similarly, no x intercept was found for the graph of $x^2 - 4x + 8 = y$. Now we can also note that the discriminants of each of these is less than zero; therefore, we know the roots are complex numbers.

In order to graph complex numbers, we must establish a plane in which each complex number corresponds to one and only one point. Recall that in the Cartesian coordinate system each point in the plane corresponded to one and only one ordered pair of numbers and that any ordered pair of numbers corresponded to one and only one point in the plane. Notice that every complex number $a + bi$ can be considered an ordered pair (a, bi). We can logically expect that these ordered pairs might serve satisfactorily as our coordinates. That is, if the horizontal axis represents the real number line and the vertical axis represents the set of imaginary numbers $\{bi\}$ (we call this the Im axis), the plane established by these two axes fulfills our requirements of "a point for every number and a number for every point." In Figure 5-1 we plot the points corresponding to the following numbers:

$0 + 3i$	(1)	$-4 + 0i$	(4)	$-3 + 3i$	(7)
$0 - 3i$	(2)	$3 + 3i$	(5)	$-3 - 3i$	(8)
$4 + 0i$	(3)	$3 - 3i$	(6)	$0 + 0i$	(9)

Figure 5-1

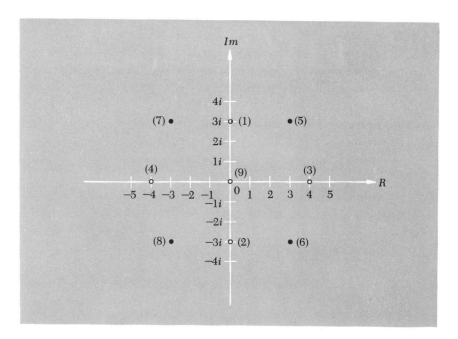

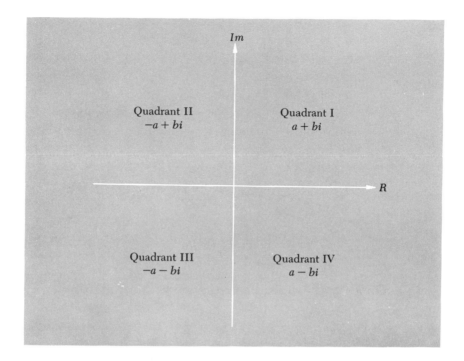

**Figure
5-2**

We call this plane the complex number plane and divide it into four quadrants. Quadrant I, as shown in Figure 5-2, contains the numbers of the form $a + bi$ $(a, b > 0)$. Quadrant II contains all numbers of the form $-a + bi$ $(a, b > 0)$. Quadrant III contains all numbers of the form $-a - bi$ $(a, b > 0)$. Quadrant IV contains all numbers of the form $a - bi$ $(a, b > 0)$. The origin is the point at which $a = 0$ and $b = 0$. All points on the R axis correspond to numbers of the form $a + 0i$, and all points on the Im axis to numbers of the form $0 + bi$.

Now we see that on a set of coordinates such as shown in Figure 5-2, given any complex number, one and only one point in the plane corresponds to this number. Similarly, every point on the plane corresponds to a complex number. The perpendiculars to the axes from any given point in the plane identify unique points on the two axes. The sum of these coordinates is a unique complex number, which we use to name the given point.

**EXERCISES
5.9**

1. Plot the points in the complex number plane associated with the following numbers.

a. $(3-2i)$ f. $(0+3i)$
b. $(4+4i)$ g. $(5-0i)$
c. $(-1+3i)$ h. $(-5-5i)$
d. $(-3+-i)$ i. $(-4i)$
e. $(1+5i)$ j. (-3)

2. Determine by inspection which quadrant each of the following will be located in.

a. $(3-2i)$ d. $(6+98i)$
b. $(-4+i)$ e. $(47-103i)$
c. $(-1-3i)$ f. $(-63-178i)$

5.10 Graphing Addition of Complex Numbers

Just as the number line proves helpful in visualizing what happens when two real numbers are added or subtracted, we can hope that the complex plane might also be helpful in this regard.

Since, by definition,

$$(a+bi)+(c+di)=(a+c)+(b+d)i$$

we can plot on the complex plane the three points which correspond to these numbers. To see this done, examine Figure 5-3.

Figure 5-3

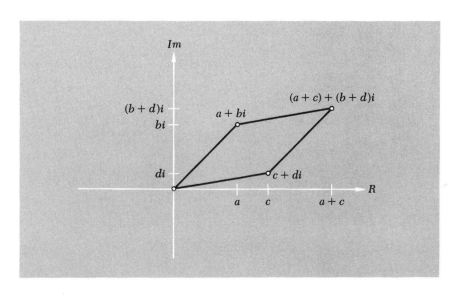

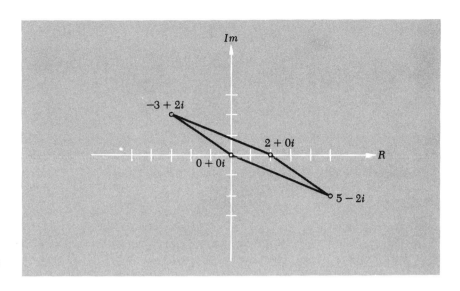

Figure 5-4

Let us now consider two other special cases. In Figure 5-4 we represent the sum

$$(-3 + 2i) + (5 - 2i) = 2 + 0i$$

and in Figure 5-5 the sum

$$(3 + 2i) + (3 - 2i) = 6$$

In all three cases we see that if the points representing the numbers are connected to the origin and to the point representing their

Figure 5-5

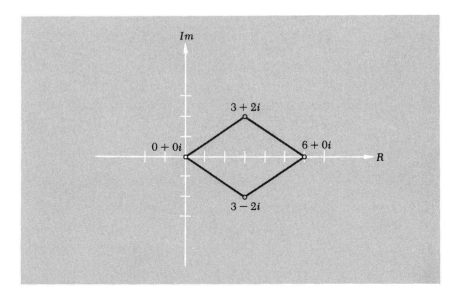

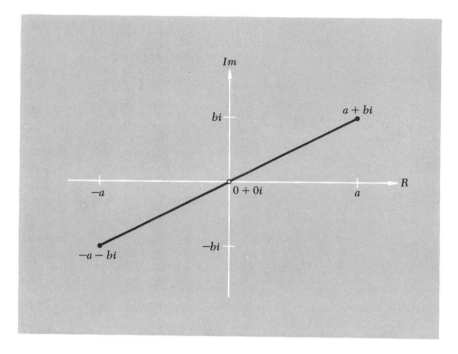

Figure
5-6

sum, a parallelogram is formed. Let us further investigate this observation by examining the graph of the general point $(a + bi)$ and its additive inverse $(-a - bi)$, as shown in Figure 5-6.

Following the above procedure, which as we have seen resulted in the construction of a parallelogram, we obtain only the straight line shown in Figure 5-6. The reason for this is that the sum of the two numbers is zero, and the point representing the sum therefore coincides with the origin. We can "show" our construction lines by slightly distorting the graph as shown in Figure 5-7. Here we have drawn another parallelogram that becomes a straight line when the length of the diagonal is zero. This special type of parallelogram, having a zero diagonal, is called a *degenerate* parallelogram.

The fact that the distance represented by the diagonal is zero together with the fact that the sum of the two numbers involved is zero might well indicate that the length of the diagonal is related to the sum of the two complex numbers. Does the hypothesis sound reasonable that the larger the numbers being added, the longer the diagonal of the parallelogram formed? Although it may not sound unreasonable, it is invalid, as you should discover when you try to test this statement. See if you can identify the main problem in testing this hypothesis. Do not check your answer until you have identified

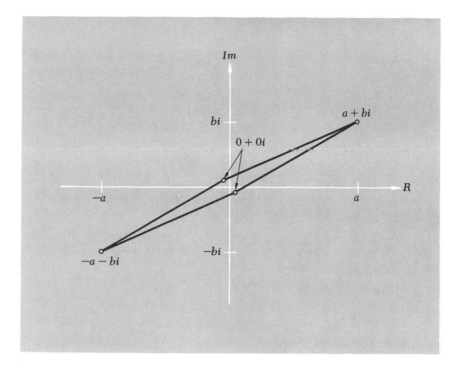

**Figure
5-7**

the problem, or have at least made a serious effort to do so. Either way, before reading further be sure to

CHECK YOUR WORK on page 191

Since graphing helped us discover that the field of complex numbers is not an *ordered* field, let us look closer at a fact suggested by the graphs shown in Figures 5-4–5-6. In each of these graphs, the sum of two complex numbers was found to identify a point on the real number line. Why is this so?

Examining Figures 5-4–5-6, we see that in each case the second term of one complex number is the additive inverse of the second term of the other complex number. Speaking of complex numbers in this way, the second term of a complex number is often called the *imaginary part* and the first the *real part*. In general, we can see that $(a + bi) + (c - bi)$ is a real number if the imaginary part of one addend is the additive inverse of the imaginary part of the other addend. In such a case the fourth point of the parallelogram always lies on the axis representing the real number line. Therefore, not only is the sum of a real number and its additive inverse a real number but there are an infinite number of complex numbers that may be added to a given complex number to yield an element of R!

For example, let us find the solution set for a and b under the condition that $(3 + 2i) + (a + bi)$ is a real number. In other words, find $\{(a, b)|(3 - 2i) + (a + bi) \in R\}$. We have just discussed the fact that $(a + bi) + (c - bi)$ is a real number; so we need only ensure that the imaginary parts are additive inverses. In this case b must equal 2, because $2i$ is the additive inverse of $-2i$. Thus, our solution set is $\{(a, b)|a \in R, b = 2\}$ – an infinite set.

We have obtained *real* numbers by adding complex numbers whose imaginary parts were additive inverses. This suggests that we should study the *product* of two such numbers. Is there a solution to the condition that $(a + bi)(c + di)$ be a real number? Can we find $\{(a, b, c, d)|(a + bi)(c + di) \in R\}$? We know from our study of multiplication (or from the application of the means and extremes rule) that $(a + bi)(c + di) = (ac - bd) + (bc + ad)i$, which can only be a real number if $bc + ad = 0$. One way of expressing our solution set, then, is $\{(a, b, c, d)|bc + ad = 0\}$. But when does $bc + ad = 0$? Only when $bc = -(ad)$.

What other conditions does this demand? Work this problem out and then

CHECK YOUR WORK on page 192

5.11 Simplifying Complex Numbers

We have shown the product of a complex number and its conjugate to be a real number, that is, $(a + bi)(a - bi) = a^2 + b^2$. This fact is particularly useful to us, since a number of the form $c + di$ is always preferred to one having a complex number in the denominator, indicating a division yet to be accomplished. Hence, to simplify an expression like $(3 + 2i)/(4 - i)$, we need only multiply this fraction by the identity $(4 + i)/(4 + i)$. Since $4 + i$ is the conjugate of the denominator, the result is a complex number over a real number, which can then be written in the form $c + di$, where $c, d \in R$. For example,

$$\frac{3 + 2i}{4 - i} = \frac{3 + 2i}{4 - i} \cdot \frac{4 + i}{4 + i} = \frac{10 + 11i}{16 + 1} = \frac{10 + 11i}{17} = \frac{10}{17} + \frac{11}{17}i$$

Notice that we have not only obtained the desired simplification, but we have accomplished the division of $(3 + 2i)$ by $(4 - i)$. Previously, we would have performed such a division by using the multiplicative inverse, as follows:

$$(3 + 2i)(4 - i)^{-1} = (3 + 2i)\left(\frac{4}{4^2 + 1^2} + \frac{-(-i)}{4^2 + 1^2}\right) = (3 + 2i)\frac{(4 + i)}{17}$$

This latter procedure is a longer, more mechanical process, dependent upon the memorized definition of the multiplicative inverse. In effect, however, it is the same procedure as multiplying the original by the identity, $(4 + i)/(4 + i)$.

Notice the similarity between multiplying the numerator and the denominator of a complex fraction by the conjugate of the denominator and the process of dividing fractions in R. To divide $\frac{3}{4}$ by $\frac{2}{3}$, we can write

$$\frac{\frac{3}{4}}{\frac{2}{3}}$$

We can now decide to multiply both the numerator and denominator by $\frac{3}{2}$ to obtain a denominator of 1:

$$\frac{\frac{3}{4} \cdot \frac{3}{2}}{\frac{2}{3} \cdot \frac{3}{2}} = \frac{\frac{3}{4} \cdot \frac{3}{2}}{\frac{6}{6}} = \frac{\frac{3}{4} \cdot \frac{3}{2}}{1} = \frac{3}{4} \cdot \frac{3}{2}$$

We can save ourselves much time by making the rule invert and multiply! Similarly in $C^\#$, to simplify or to divide two numbers such as $(1 + i)/(2 + 3i)$, we decide to multiply the numerator and denominator by $(2 - 3i)$, the conjugate of the denominator. This, in effect, provides us with the multiplicative inverse and our previous description of division as seen in the second step below:

$$\frac{(1 + i)}{(2 + 3i)} \cdot \frac{(2 - 3i)}{(2 - 3i)} = (1 + i)\left(\frac{2}{4 + 9} + \frac{-3i}{4 + 9}\right)$$
$$= (1 + i)\frac{(2 - 3i)}{13} = \frac{5 - i}{13} = \frac{5}{13} - \frac{1}{13}i$$

Eliminating the second step, we can simply proceed as follows:

$$\frac{(1 + i)}{(2 + 3i)}\frac{(2 - 3i)}{(2 - 3i)} = \frac{5 - i}{4 + 9} = \frac{5}{13} - \frac{1}{13}i$$

We have explored our new system $C^\#$ to see how workable it is, that is, to see if we can compute and solve problems in this universe. Have we done enough to permit us to solve problems in $C^\#$ similar to the problems in R that are ordinarily solved in the elementary schools? Let us try.

Suppose we wish to find the value of

$$\frac{3 + 2i}{4 - i} + \frac{1 + i}{2 + 3i}$$

We first multiply the numerator and denominator of each fraction by the conjugate of its denominator.

$$\frac{(3 + 2i)(4 + i)}{(4 - i)(4 + i)} + \frac{(1 + i)(2 - 3i)}{(2 + 3i)(2 - 3i)} = \frac{10 + 11i}{17} + \frac{5 - i}{13}$$

$$= \frac{130 + 143i}{221} + \frac{85 - 17i}{221} \qquad \text{(How did we obtain this common denominator?)}$$

$$= \frac{215}{221} + \frac{126}{221} i$$

The result is a complex number in the form $c + di$ ($c, d \in R$). There are at least two other ways that would do just as well in solving this problem. Solve the problem in at least one other way, and then

CHECK YOUR WORK on page 193

EXERCISES
5.11

Simplify:

1. $\dfrac{(3 - i)}{(3 + i)}$

2. $\dfrac{(2 + 3i)}{(3 - 4i)}$

3. $\dfrac{(3 - 2i) - (2 + 3i)}{(3 - 5i)}$

4. $\dfrac{i(4 - i)}{(2 - 4i)}$

5. $\dfrac{(2 - i)}{(3 + 2i)} + \dfrac{(4 + i)}{(5 - i)}$

6. $\dfrac{(1 + 2i)}{(4 - 3i)} - \dfrac{(2 - 3i)}{(1 + i)}$

7. $\dfrac{(16 + 19i) - (14 + 19i)}{(1 + i)(1 - i)} + \dfrac{(17 + i) - (17 - i)}{(1 - 2i)}$

SUMMARY

We have now developed the field $C^\#$ as far as we need it for our purposes. Let us summarize what we have done and what our purposes were.

1. We expanded R to $C^\#$.

2. We assured ourselves that $C^\#$ is a field.

3. We discovered that $C^\#$ is not an *ordered* field as R was found to be.

4. We found that we could compute in $C^\#$, just as we did in R.

5. Our purpose was to gain closure under the operation of taking the square root so that we can solve any quadratic equation, even if the discriminant is negative. We found that $C^\#$ provides the needed closure.

The many parallels and the important differences in computational procedures that we discovered between $C^\#$ and R help us obtain a greater insight into the system of rational numbers, our basic tool in the elementary school. All of us should now appreciate the power of the distributive property. We can appreciate its value in mathematics from its first unsophisticated use in the elementary school all the way through college programs. We can call the distributive property the "work horse" of algebra and really mean it!

The development of $C^\#$ provides us with a better appreciation of the meaning of a field and a better understanding of the importance of an *ordered* field such as R. We can now appreciate the possibility that other systems or fields may be developed that might prove most valuable to some science in the future. We can now accept the fact that $C^\#$ is indispensable in many areas of science such as electrical engineering. The development of other systems with no present practical application becomes understandable and makes the old question apply—which came first the chicken or the egg? Does a practical problem in science demand and motivate the development of a number system, or do we find practical applications for existing systems. Which idea do you prefer?

At any rate, the development of $C^\#$ has provided us with a set that is closed under the operation of taking the square root. Once more, the man-developed thought processes aspect of all mathematics is brought clearly into focus. Our appreciation of the orderliness and elegance of systematic development from a set of postulates has been reinforced. If nothing else, the structure of mathematics should *not* now appear to you as a forbidding, incomprehensible, formidable subject, which is too hard. You should now see it from a higher level of appreciation, knowing that because of its innate reasonableness any aspect of it can be understood by most of you if you have the time and inclination to study and assimilate the ideas involved.

We conclude by realizing that algebra is a logical subject—a straightforward subject—the science of dealing in a most general way with a set of numbers, operations, and properties.

CHAPTER REVIEW TEST ———————————

Multiply the following expressions.

1. $(2 + 3i)(3 - 2i)$ 3. $i(2 + i)$

2. $(-4 + i)(3 - i)$ 4. $(3 + 4i)(-2 - 3i)$

Simplify the following expressions.

5. $\dfrac{3 + i}{i}$ 7. $\dfrac{2 + 3i}{2 - 3i}$

6. $3 + \dfrac{2}{3 + i}$ 8. $\dfrac{4 - 2i}{-3 + 5i} + \dfrac{1 + i}{1 - i}$

Graph the following sums on axes R and Im.

9. $(3 + 2i) + (-4 + 3i)$
10. $(4 - 3i) + (4 + 3i)$

11. Prove that i^{-1} is also the additive inverse of i; prove that $-i$ is both the additive and multiplicative inverse of i.

12. Define $C^{\#}$ and show by illustration that it satisfies each of the field properties.

13. Prove that $C^{\#}$ satisfies the commutative property of multiplication.

Prove that the following statements are true.

14. $C^{\#}$ is closed under addition.
15. $C^{\#}$ is closed under multiplication.
16. $C^{\#}$ is closed under division (the divisor not zero).

17. List the conditions under which division in $C^{\#}$ yields an element of R!

18. List one condition under which subtraction in $C^\#$ always results in an element of R.

Define the following terms.

19. conjugate
20. discriminant

Identify *all* sets from I, R, and $C^\#$ in which each of the following equations can be solved for x.

21. $x^2 + 1 = 0$ 23. $5x^2 - x - 1 = 0$
22. $x^2 - 1 = 0$ 24. $2x^2 - 4x + 3 = 0$

25. Can you invent an operation under which $C^\#$ is not closed?

CHECKING YOUR WORK

page 166

1. Yes, the set R is a proper subset of

$$\{a + bi \mid a, b \in R \text{ and } i = \sqrt{-1}\}.$$

Whenever $b = 0$, $a + bi = a$, and the element a is an element of R.

2. Yes, $\{i\}$ is a proper subset of the set, for whenever $a = 0$, $a + bi = 0 + bi = bi$, and if $b = 1$, then by the identity properties $a + bi = i$ when $a = 0$, $b = 1$.

3. Let us add the two numbers $a + bi$ and $c + di$ according to the field properties of R.

$$
\begin{aligned}
(a + bi) + (c + di) &= a + bi + c + di && \text{(associative property)} \\
&= a + c + bi + di && \text{(commutative property)} \\
&= (a + c) + (bi + di) && \text{(associative property)} \\
&= (a + c) + (b + d)i && \text{(distributive property)}
\end{aligned}
$$

We conclude that $(a + bi) + (c + di) = (a + c) + (b + d)i$. Note that addition in this set means finding the sum of the real values of each number and adding this sum to the total number of i's in the two numbers. As in elementary arithmetic, we can develop an algorithm for addition as follows:

$$a + bi$$
$$+ \quad \underline{c + di}$$
$$(a + c) + (b + d)i$$

4. Yes, the set is closed under addition. We have shown in the above discussion that

$$(a + bi) + (c + di) = (a + c) + (b + d)i$$

Since R is closed under addition, we can let $(a + c) = k$ and $(b + d) = m$; $k, m \in R$. Therefore

$$(a + bi) + (c + di) = k + mi$$

The last equation shows that $C^\#$ is closed under addition. Do we need to test the cases for $k = 0$ or $m = 0$? Do it and see.

Return to page 166

page 171

To show that the associative property of multiplication in $C^\#$ holds, we must show that

$$[(a + bi)(c + di)](e + fi) = (a + bi)[(c + di)(e + fi)]$$

Applying the rule for multiplication twice as indicated on both sides of the equation, we find

$$[(ac - bd) + (bc + ad)i](e + fi) = (a + bi)[(ce - df) + (de + cf)i]$$
$$[(ac - bd)e - (bc + ad)f] + [(bc + ad)e + (ac - bd)f]i$$
$$= [a(ce - df) - b(de + cf)] + [b(ce - df) + a(de + cf)]i$$

Applying the distributive property to both sides of the equation, we eliminate many of the parentheses. (Why can we use the distributive property here when we have not shown that it holds in $C^\#$? Because we are applying it only to elements of R.)

$$(ace - bde - bcf - adf) + (bce + ade + acf - bdf)i$$
$$= (ace - adf - bde - bcf) + (bce - bdf + ade + acf)i$$

We can commute real numbers on the left-hand side to show the two sides of the equation to be equal.

$$(ace - adf - bde - bcf) + (bce - bdf + ade + acf)i$$

Return to page 171

page 172

We need to find values of c and d such that:

$(a + bi)(c + di) = 1$

$(ac - bd) + (bc + ad)i = 1$ (definition of multiplication in $C^\#$)

$(ac - bd) + (bc + ad)i = 1 + 0i$ (property 4a)

Hence

$$\begin{cases} ac - bd = 1 \\ bc + ad = 0 \end{cases} \tag{1}$$
$$\tag{2}$$

$$\begin{cases} a^2c - abd = a & \text{(multiplying (1) by } a) \\ b^2c + abd = 0 & \text{(multiplying (2) by } b) \end{cases} \tag{3}$$
$$\tag{4}$$

$$a^2c + b^2c = a \qquad \text{(adding (3) and (4))} \tag{5}$$

$$(a^2 + b^2)c = a \qquad \text{(distributive property)}$$

$$c = \frac{a}{a^2 + b^2}, \qquad (a^2 + b^2) \neq 0$$

Substituting this value of c in equation (2) and solving for d, we find

$$b \cdot \frac{a}{a^2 + b^2} + ad = 0 \qquad \text{(substitution for } c)$$

$$ad = \frac{-ab}{a^2 + b^2} \qquad \text{(additive inverse added to both sides)}$$

$$d = \frac{-ab}{a(a^2 + b^2)} = \frac{-b}{a^2 + b^2} \qquad \text{(dividing both sides by } a)$$

Having found values for c and d, we can now write

$$c + di = \frac{a}{a^2 + b^2} + \left(\frac{-b}{a^2 + b^2} \right) i$$

where

$$(a^2 + b^2) \neq 0$$

Thus, we have shown the multiplicative inverse for $(a + bi)$ to be

$$(a + bi)^{-1} = \frac{a}{a^2 + b^2} + \left(\frac{-b}{a^2 + b^2} \right) i$$

Return to page 172

page 183

One of the main problems is to define the meaning of *larger*. When is one complex number larger than another? When does $a + bi < c + di$ have meaning if $b, d \neq 0$? Is $a + bi$ *ever* less than $c + di$? Recall that in the field of real numbers this relation was both useful and meaningful. We know that $a < b$ if and only if $a + c = b$ $(c > 0)$. This theorem was the result of the ordered property of the real number system. R is an *ordered* field. We have shown $C^{\#}$ to be a field. Have we lost the ordered property in expanding from R to $C^{\#}$? Let us see.

Accepting the same definition of the relation "is less than" that we used in R, let us prove that $C^{\#}$ is either ordered or not ordered. Assume it is ordered. Then

$$(a + bi) < (c + di) \Longleftrightarrow (a + bi) + k = (c + di)$$

where $k > 0$ and $b, d \neq 0$.

$$a + bi + k = c + di$$
$$a + k - c = di - bi$$
$$a + k - c = (d - b)i$$

$$\frac{a + k + c}{d - b} = i \quad \text{(where } d \neq b)$$

But this is a contradiction. Because of closure, the left-hand side of the equation is a real number and therefore cannot be equal to i, because i is not an element of R.

Well, perhaps then we should have assumed that $a + bi$ is the larger of the two numbers. Let us see. If

$$(a + bi) > (c + di)$$

then

$$a + bi = c + di + k \quad (k > 0)$$
$$bi - di = c + k - a$$

$$i = \frac{c + k - a}{b - d} \quad (b \neq d)$$

Again we have arrived at a similar contradiction.

We *have* lost the ordered property! Therefore, in $C^{\#}$ it is meaningless to say that one number is greater or smaller than another!

Return to page 183

page
184

If $bc = -(ad)$, then one possibility is that $c + di$ be the *conjugate* of $a + bi$. That is, $c = a$ and $d = -b$. The conjugate of a complex number is defined to have the same real part and the additive inverse of the imaginary part of the complex number. The conjugate of $a + bi$ is $a - bi$. So if $c = a$ and $d = -b$, our solution set can be written as $\{(a, b, c, d) | a = c, \quad b = -d\}$. Let us verify this.

$(a + bi)(a - bi) = (a^2 + b^2) + (ab - ab)i = a^2 + b^2$

which is a real number! Does this tell us what happens when we multiply a complex number by its multiplicative inverse? Is there a relation between this result and the definition of the multiplicative inverse of $a + bi$ as $a/(a^2 + b^2) + [-b/(a^2 + b^2)]i$? Before continuing, try to answer this question.

Another possibility of obtaining a real number as the product of two complex numbers arises when $b = a$ and $d = -c$. Is $bc = -(ad)$ in this case? Yes it is! Substituting these relations in $(a + bi)(c + di)$, we obtain $(a + ai)(c - ci)$. Factoring out the common real factor of each number, we obtain $[a(1 + i)][c(1 - i)]$ or $ac(1 + i)(1 - i)$. Consequently, we see that the condition $b = a$ and $d = -c$ always reduces to the special case

$$ac(1 + i)(1 - i) = ac(1 - i^2) = ac(2) = 2ac$$

a real number, indeed!

The remaining possibilities that $bc = -ad$ involve zero. Can you list at least one condition involving zero, where the product of two complex numbers is a real number?

Return to page 184

page 186

$$\frac{3 + 2i}{4 - i} + \frac{1 + i}{2 + 3i} = \frac{(3 + 2i)(2 + 3i)}{(4 - i)(2 + 3i)} + \frac{(1 + i)(4 - i)}{(2 + 3i)(4 - i)}$$
$$= \frac{13i}{11 + 10i} + \frac{5 + 3i}{11 + 10i} = \frac{5 + 16i}{11 + 10i} = \frac{(5 + 16i)(11 - 10i)}{(11 + 10i)(11 - 10i)}$$
$$= \frac{55 + 160 + (176 - 50)i}{121 + 100} = \frac{215 + 126i}{221} = \frac{215}{221} + \frac{126}{221}i$$

Here we first found a common denominator and added, then divided by multiplying the numerator and denominator by the complex conjugate of the denominator.

This is the same procedure we followed when adding

$$\tfrac{2}{3} + \tfrac{3}{4} = \tfrac{2}{3} \cdot \tfrac{4}{4} + \tfrac{3}{4} \cdot \tfrac{3}{3} = \tfrac{8}{12} + \tfrac{9}{12} = \tfrac{17}{12}$$

Can you point out the parallels between the two procedures and their solutions?

Return to page 186

6

OTHER TOPICS

There are many *mathematical systems* such as groups, rings, and fields with which people work today. We have already examined the *field* of rational numbers, the *field* of real numbers, and the *field* of complex numbers. Thus we are better aquainted with the field properties than with the properties of groups and rings. The purpose of this section is to show that a field is not the only type of mathematical system that can be examined and that there are other systems of numbers besides Ra, R, and $C^\#$ that are fields.

6.1 Mathematical Systems

A good definition of a field must be written in general terms. When we were reviewing the meaning of a field (see pp. 160, 161), we used the familiar operations of addition and multiplication and the set R as our reference set. Replacing these with general terms we can define a field as follows:

DEFINITION 6-1 ────────────────────────────────────

A **field** is a set S containing at least two elements and having the following properties:

1. S is closed under two binary operations # and *, which we refer to as "addition" and "multiplication," respectively.

2. The associative property holds for both operations. For all $a, b, c \in S$,

   $a \mathbin{\#} (b \mathbin{\#} c) = (a \mathbin{\#} b) \mathbin{\#} c$

   and

   $a * (b * c) = (a * b) * c$

3. The commutative property holds for both operations. For all $a, b \in S$,

   $a \mathbin{\#} b = b \mathbin{\#} a$ and $a * b = b * a$

4. Identity elements, denoted by θ and Δ, exist such that for all $a \in S$,

   $a \mathbin{\#} \theta = a$ and $a * \Delta = a$

5. Inverse elements $-a$ and $1/a$ exist such that for all $a \in S$,

   $a \mathbin{\#} (-a) = \theta$ and $a * \dfrac{1}{a} = \Delta$ $(a \ne \theta)$

6. The distributive property holds in that $*$ distributes over $\#$. For all $a, b, c \in S$,

   $a * (b \mathbin{\#} c) = (a * b) \mathbin{\#} (a * c)$

Note in particular that

1. the additive identity θ is obtained when an element and its additive inverse are added;

2. the multiplicative identity Δ is obtained when an element is multiplied by its multiplicative inverse; and

3. the identities need not be our old friends 0 and 1 in all fields.

Let us examine two systems to see if they meet the criteria of a field. First we examine a system with just two elements, since the definition demands that we must have at least two elements.

Given the set $S = \{0, 1\}$ together with the binary operations of $+$ and $\cdot$ as defined in the following tables, do we have a field?

You should recall from your earlier work in different bases that we can construct the addition and multiplication table in base two as shown in Table 6-1.

Table
6-1

ADDITION AND MULTIPLICATION TABLES

+	0	1
0	0	1
1	1	10

×	0	1
0	0	0
1	0	1

1. S is closed under multiplication but is not closed under addition. (The number 10 is not in S. This flaw alone is enough to ensure that our system is *not* a field.)

2. The associative property holds for multiplication. For example, $0 \cdot (1 \cdot 0) = (0 \cdot 1) \cdot 0$.

3. The commutative property holds for multiplication. For example, $0 \cdot 1 = 1 \cdot 0$.

4. Identity elements 0 and 1 exist such that $0 + 0 = 0$ and $1 + 0 = 1$; $1 \cdot 1 = 1$ and $0 \cdot 1 = 0$.

5. The multiplicative inverse exists in that $1 \cdot 1 = 1$. The additive inverse does not exist, since no replacement for a can be found such that $1 + a = 0$. (Of course, -1 would be a suitable replacement, but -1 is not in S.)

6. Why didn't we check properties 2 and 3 for addition? Why didn't we test the distributive property?

We know from statements 1 and 5 that this number system is not a field.

Is the set of integers modulo 5 a field? Perhaps we should first review the idea of modulus before trying to answer this question. Modulo arithmetic is most commonly met in clock arithmetic. If it is 6 o'clock now, 8 hours from now it will be 14 o'clock. But most clocks only have 12 elements in the set of numbers; so we say that 8 hours from now it will be 2 o'clock. In this sense, when we add 6 and 8 in clock arithmetic, we obtain $6 + 8 = 2$. Similarly,

$$11 + 4 = 3$$
$$3 + 6 + 8 = 5$$

Actually we are dealing with counting numbers that are remainders after we have *divided by 12*. Modulo arithmetic is based upon the same concept of remainders. The two operations in modulo arithmetic are not our *usual* addition (+) and multiplication (·) operations. If we work with the integers modulo 5, we define "addition" as the process of adding (in the usual sense) two elements of S and then finding the remainder when the sum is divided by 5. For example, in the integers modulo 5:

$$3 + 4 + 2 = 4 \qquad (9 \div 5 = 1, \text{ with 4 remainder})$$
$$1 + 4 = 0 \qquad (5 \div 5 = 1, \text{ with 0 remainder})$$

Notice that in such modulo work zero replaces n in modulo n, and we always have exactly n elements in the set, including zero. Thus, modulo 8 is a system in which

$$S = \{0, 1, 2, 3, 4, 5, 6, 7\}$$

and modulo 5 is a system in which $S = \{0, 1, 2, 3, 4\}$.

"Multiplication" can now be defined for modulo 5 as the process of multiplying two elements of S and then finding the remainder when that product is divided by 5. Thus, in modulo 5

$$3 \cdot 4 = 2 \qquad (12 \div 5 = 2 \text{ with 2 remainder})$$
$$(4 \cdot 4) \cdot 2 = 2 \qquad ((16 \div 5) \cdot 2, \text{ or } 1 \cdot 2 = 2)$$

We can now address ourselves to the question whether or not the set of integers modulo 5 is a field. Let us begin by calling this system I_5 and construct its addition and multiplication tables. (In general, we refer to the set of integers modulo n as I_n.) Since we have defined addition in a way that is different from the usual interpretation, we do not use the regular plus sign $+$ to indicate the operation. We arbitrarily select the sign "circle plus" $\oplus$. Similarly, we use the sign "circle cross" $\otimes$ for multiplication.

Table 6-2 I_5 **ADDITION AND MULTIPLICATION TABLES**

$\oplus$	0	1	2	3	4
0	0	1	2	3	4
1	1	2	3	4	0
2	2	3	4	0	1
3	3	4	0	1	2
4	4	0	1	2	3

$\otimes$	0	1	2	3	4
0	0	0	0	0	0
1	0	1	2	3	4
2	0	2	4	1	3
3	0	3	1	4	2
4	0	4	3	2	1

Table 6-2 clearly shows that the set $\{0, 1, 2, 3, 4\}$, which we label S, is closed under both operations, because all sums and products possible are elements of S. Similarly, the tables can be used to show that for each a, b, and c in S

$$a \oplus (b \oplus c) = (a \oplus b) \oplus c$$

and

$$a \otimes (b \otimes c) - (a \otimes b) \otimes c$$

Hence, the associative property holds for both operations.

That the commutative property holds for both operations is even easier to verify from Table 6-2. Try it.

An additive identity exists. The table shows that for each a in S added to zero (the additive identity in this case) the result is a. The multiplicative identity proves to be the element 1 because the product of 1 and each a in S is a.

An additive inverse exists in S for each a in S.

The addition table shows that for each a in S there exists another element such that the sum of the two elements is the additive identity (in this case, 0). We note that

$$0 + 0 = 0$$
$$1 + 4 = 0$$
$$2 + 3 = 0$$
$$3 + 2 = 0$$
$$4 + 1 = 0$$

A multiplicative inverse exists in S for each nonzero element. This fact can be verified through a tabulation of products equal to 1, as shown in the multiplication table.

The distributive property can be verified. Only one example is given here:

$$2 \otimes (4 \oplus 3) = 2 \otimes (2) = 4$$
$$(2 \otimes 4) \oplus (2 \otimes 3) = 3 \oplus 1 = 4$$

and, therefore,

$$2 \otimes (4 \oplus 3) = (2 \otimes 4) \oplus (2 \otimes 3)$$

We conclude that I_5 is indeed a field. Does this suggest the possibility that I_n is a field for any n greater than 1? (We say n must be greater than 1, because any field must have at least 2 elements.) If we investigated this possibility fully, we would find that all such systems would *not* be fields. Indeed, only in the case where n is a prime number do we have a field. We will not go this far in our investigation, but it is worthwhile for us to examine one nonprime n. Let us investigate I_4 to find out how it fails to meet the criteria of a field. We begin once again by constructing the addition and multiplication tables — this time for I_4, the set S being $\{0, 1, 2, 3\}$.

Table 6-3 I_4 **ADDITION AND MULTIPLICATION TABLES**

$\oplus$	0	1	2	3
0	0	1	2	3
1	1	2	3	0
2	2	3	0	1
3	3	0	1	2

$\otimes$	0	1	2	3
0	0	0	0	0
1	0	1	2	3
2	0	2	0	2
3	0	3	2	1

Using Table 6-3, follow the same procedures as you did in examining I_5, and determine why I_4 is not a field. After you have done so, or after you have spent sufficient time on the problem

CHECK YOUR WORK on page 215

What is the meaning of our answer in the preceding check your work section? Since I_4 was shown to satisfy all the field properties except the requirement that every nonzero element must have a multiplicative inverse, what can you say about the four fundamental operations in I_4? One of the rewards of working with a number system that is a field is that the set is closed under all four operations: addition, subtraction, multiplication, and division (the divisor not zero). Recall that it was the multiplicative inverse that made division in Ra possible. Does this mean we can divide in I_4? Table 6-3 shows that the product of 2 and 3 is 2. Therefore, 2 divided by 3 must be 2. Similarly, since $1 \otimes 2 = 2$, then $2 \div 1 = 2$.

Suppose you are confronted with the linear equation

$$2 \otimes m = 3$$

in I_4 and you wish to solve for m. An examination of the multiplication table for I_4 reveals that there is no replacement for m such that the product of 2 and m is 3. Finding no such replacement, we might rely on intuition and decide to divide both sides by 2, since surely $2 \div 2$ must be 1 (it always has been that in the past!). We then obtain

$$m = \tfrac{3}{2}$$

a rational number that is not an element of S. Thus $3 \div 2 = m \notin S$, and therefore S is not closed under division in I_4. In short, S is not closed under division in I_4 because the field property of the multiplicative inverse is not realized.

In summary we should remember that:

1. Many mathematical systems are not fields.

2. Many mathematical systems other than Ra, R, and $C^\#$ are fields.

3. The additive identity need not always be the symbol 0 (as can be seen in problem 6.1-2b).

4. The multiplicative identity is not always the symbol 1 (see problem 6.1-2c).

5. The additive inverse property demands that for each element of the set, there exist an element such that the sum of the two is the additive identity.

6. The multiplicative inverse property demands that for each element (excluding the additive identity) of the set there exist an element such that the product of the two is the multiplicative identity.

EXERCISES
6.1

1. Construct the addition and multiplication tables for I_7.

2. Given $D = \{x, y, z\}$, and the operations # and * and the following tables:

#	x	y	z
x	z	x	y
y	x	y	z
z	y	z	x

*	x	y	z
x	z	y	x
y	y	y	y
z	x	y	z

    a. Show that the system D satisfies the commutative property for both operations.

    b. Find the identity for #.

    c. Find the identity for *.

    d. Given that the system D meets all the criteria of a field, find the value of $(x * y) \# [z * (x \# y)]$.

    e. Solve $(x * a) \# (x * z) = z * (x \# y)$ for a.

    f. Solve $(y * z) \# 2 = x \# y \# z$ for 2.

3. In set D of problem 2, replace the additive identity with the symbol 0, the multiplicative identity with the symbol 1, and the third element of D with the symbol 2; replace # with $\oplus$ and replace * with $\otimes$. Is your new system I_3?

6.2   Absolute Value

The *absolute value* of a number refers to the magnitude of the number regardless of its sign. If r is a real number, its magnitude is simply its (positive) distance from 0 along the real line. To indicate absolute value, the given number is usually enclosed between two vertical lines. Therefore, the absolute value of a is represented by the symbol $|a|$; the absolute value of -9 is written $|-9|$ and equals 9; and the absolute value of 6 is written $|6| = 6$.

    Absolute values are commonly used in discussing distances between points. If the question is: "how far apart are Denver, Colorado and Las Cruces, New Mexico?," our response is 637 miles. The distance is the same whether we are going from Las Cruces to Denver or from Denver to Las Cruces. Similarly, if we must say how far -3 is from 4 on the number line, we say 7 and not -7.

    The absolute value concept is nothing more than a rule and might be viewed as a function. The images under the absolute value function are nonnegative numbers in every case. If k is a positive real number, its image under the absolute value function is k. If k is 0, its image is 0; if k is a negative real number, its image is $-k$. Thus, if $k = -3$, its image is $-(-3)$ or 3. We illustrate this fact by writing $|-3| = 3$ and read it as "the absolute value of -3 is 3."

    In short, the abolute value of a nonnegative real number is the number itself, while the absolute value of a negative real number is its additive inverse. This can be expressed by the following two conditions:

if $a \geqq 0$, then $|a| = a$
if $a < 0$, then $|a| = -a$

The absolute value function has many uses. We are using the function each time we guess the number of beans (or pennies, or ping-pong balls) in a large container with the understanding that he who guesses closest to the exact number will be the winner. We care not whether our guess is less or more than the exact number; we care only if the absolute value of the difference between our guess and the exact number is the smallest absolute value resulting from all the guesses. If there are exactly 867 beans in a jar, and you guessed 798 and I guessed 939, we would decide the winner by computing:

for you: $867 - 798 = 69$,
for me: $867 - 939 = -72$,

but

$|-72| = 72$

So you are the winner since your guess was only 69 away from the exact number of beans, while mine was 72.

We use this concept in multiplying in arithmetic. When we multiply -7×6, we first multiply the two absolute values and then affix the proper sign. We do the same in multiplying two negative numbers; to solve -12×-8, we first find the product of the absolute values to be 96, and then decide that the sign of the product is positive.

Can you find the solution set of integers for the condition

$|x| < 3$

Since the absolute value of $-2, -1, 0, 1,$ and 2 is in each case less than 3, the solution set is $\{-2, -1, 0, 1, 2\}$.

A more difficult problem is to find the solution set in I for the condition

$|x - 3| < 3$

Your solution set probably contains the elements 5, 4, 3, does it not? But there are other elements in the solution set, namely, 2 and 1. Notice that $|1 - 3| = |-2| = 2$, which is less than 3. The solution set is $\{1, 2, 3, 4, 5\}$.

EXERCISES
6.2

Find the solution set of integers satisfying the following conditions:

1. $|x| = 2$
2. $|x| \leq 5$
3. $|x| < 2$
4. $|x + 1| < 3$
5. $|x - 1| \leq 3$
6. $|x| \geq 3$

7. $|x + 1| > 2$
8. $|3x + 1| > 12$
9. $|2y + 2| \leq 8$
10. $3 \leq |1 - x|$ and $|2x + 1| < 6$
11. $|3x + 2| \leq 11$ and $6 < |2x + 1|$
12. $15 \leq |2x - 3| < 21$

13. Tabulate the elements of the intersection of the set of integers and the set A, where $A = \{x \mid 2 > |x|\}$.

6.3 Graphing the Absolute Value Function

Finally, let us view the absolute value function through the process of graphing. Consider $y = |x + 1|$. If this were simply a linear equation without the absolute value sign, the graph for the equation $(y = x + 1)$ would be drawn as in Figure 6-1.

Figure
6-1

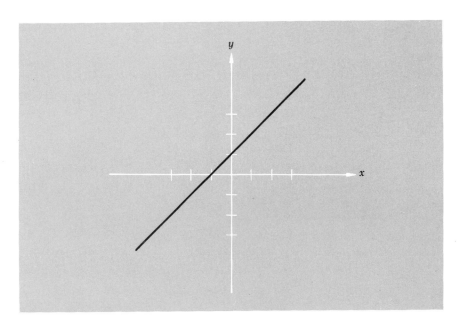

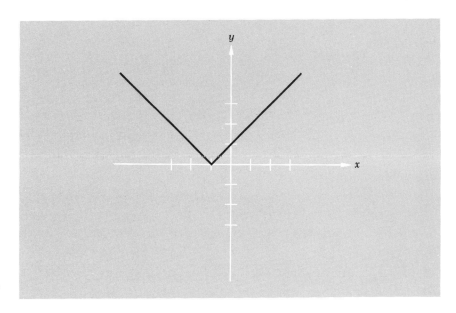

Figure 6-2

However, when x is replaced by a negative value in the equation $y = |x + 1|$, the absolute value function provides that the corresponding value of y is always positive, so that our graph now appears as shown in Figure 6-2.

EXERCISES 6.3

Sketch the graph for each of the following equations:

1. $y = |x|$
2. $y = |x + 1|$
3. $y = |x - 1|$
4. $y = |x| + 1$
5. $|2 - x| = y$

6. Sketch the graph of the condition $|2 - x| \leq y$.

7. a. Superimpose on the sketch for problem 6 the graph of

$$3y \leq |2x + 3|$$

   b. Indicate on your sketch the area containing the points whose coordinates would satisfy both conditions.

6.4   The Binomial Theorem

In Chapter 3, we multiplied binomials by using the means and extremes rule. Special factor II referred to the square of a binomial, and we learned that $(a + b)^2 = a^2 + 2ab + b^2$. We can find the cube of a binomial by multiplying

$$\begin{aligned}
(a + b)^3 &= (a + b)(a + b)(a + b) \\
&= (a^2 + 2ab + b^2)(a + b) \\
&= a^3 + 3a^2b + 3ab^2 + b^3
\end{aligned}$$

The product of the last two factors was found by using the general multiplication algorithm:

$$\begin{array}{r}
a^2 + 2ab + b^2 \\
a + b \\
\hline
a^2b + 2ab^2 + b^3 \\
a^3 + 2a^2b + ab^2 \\
\hline
a^3 + 3a^2b + 3ab^2 + b^3
\end{array}$$

We could find the 10th power of the binomial $(a + b)$ in this manner if we were patient enough and made no careless errors in the lengthy computation. As is always the case in algebra, when we reach a stage like this, we naturally seek a generalized statement, or formula, that reduces the work, and minimizes the number of operations.
   Consider the expansion of $(a + b)^n$ for $n = 1, 2, 3, 4,$ and 5.

$$(a + b)^1 = a + b$$
$$(a + b)^2 = a^2 + 2ab + b^2$$
$$(a + b)^3 = a^3 + 3a^2b + 3ab^2 + b^3$$
$$(a + b)^4 = a^4 + 4a^3b + 6a^2b^2 + 4ab^3 + b^4$$
$$(a + b)^5 = a^5 + 5a^4b + 10a^3b^2 + 10a^2b^3 + 5ab^4 + b^5$$

From these solutions we can easily recognize a general pattern for the first and last terms. The first term is always a^n, and the last is always b^n. Similarly, the coefficients of the second and next to last terms are always n. However, the coefficients of the middle terms in the expansions of the higher powers of the binomial are not so readily generalized. We can obtain these coefficients by the following rule. *By multiplying the coefficient of a term by the power of a in the term and then dividing that product by the number of that term, the coefficient of the following term is obtained.*
   These generalizations can be summarized as follows:

   1. The first term is always a^n, and in each other term the exponent of a is one less than in the preceding term.

2. The last term is always b^n, and in each other term the exponent of b is always one less than the following term.

3. Multiplying the coefficient of a term by the power of a in that term and then dividing the product by the number of the term always yields the coefficient of the next term.

For example, in applying the three preceding statements to the expansion of $(a + b)^5$ we find the first term is a^5 according to statement 1. The second term is $5a^4b$, the coefficient being found from statement 3 as $1 \cdot 5/1 = 5$. The coefficient of the third term is $5 \cdot 4/2 = 10$. Hence, the third term is $10a^3b^2$. The next coefficient is found to be $10 \cdot 3/3$ or 10, and the fourth term is $10a^2b^3$. Continuation of this process yields

$$(a + b)^5 = a^5 + 5a^4b + 10a^3b^2 + 10a^2b^3 + 5ab^4 + b^5$$

See how well you can apply the three statements to the expansion of $(a + b)^6$ and $(a + b)^7$, and then

CHECK YOUR WORK on page 216

The *binomial theorem* states that the above three generalizations hold for *any* positive integer n.

THEOREM 6-1 ───

The Binomial Theorem: Given n, a positive integer, and any real numbers a and b, then

$$(a + b)^n = a^n + na^{(n-1)}b + \frac{n(n-1)}{2} a^{(n-2)}b^2 + \frac{n(n-1)(n-2)}{2 \cdot 3} a^{(n-3)}b^3$$
$$+ \frac{n(n-1)(n-2)(n-3)}{2 \cdot 3 \cdot 4} a^{(n-4)}b^4 + \cdots + b^n$$

───

EXERCISES
6.4

Use the binomial theorem to write the expansion of:

1. $(a + b)^8$ 3. $(3 + \frac{1}{4})^3$
2. $(x + 2)^5$ 4. $(x + \frac{1}{2})^4$

5. Write the fourth term of the expansion of $(a + b)^{12}$.

6. Find $(3\frac{1}{4})^3$ and compare your work with problem 3.

7. Given the coefficients obtained in the binomial expansions below,

$(a + b)^0$								1								
$(a + b)^1$							1		1							
$(a + b)^2$						1		2		1						
$(a + b)^3$					1		3		3		1					
$(a + b)^4$				1		4		6		4		1				
$(a + b)^5$			1		5		10		10		5		1			
$(a + b)^6$		1		6		15		20		15		6		1		
$(a + b)^7$	1		7		21		35		35		21		7		1	
$(a + b)^8$	1	8		28		56		70		56		28		8		1

find a pattern that permits you to write the next two rows corresponding to powers of 9 and 10 with very little computation.

6.5 *n* Factorial

Factorial n is the number obtained by multiplying together all the integers from 1 to n inclusive, where n is a positive integer. The usual symbol for factorial is the exclamation point !, and we read 6! as "six factorial" or "factorial six."

$$6! = 1 \cdot 2 \cdot 3 \cdot 4 \cdot 5 \cdot 6 = 720$$

Factorials are useful and are widely used in mathematics. For example, the formula for finding the number of permutations of n different things taken n times is $n!$ If we need to know how many different ways 5 children can be seated in the first row of 5 desks, we compute 5!, and find the answer to be $1 \cdot 2 \cdot 3 \cdot 4 \cdot 5 = 120$, or 120 different ways.

If we need to know how many different teams of 3 on a team can be chosen from six children, we use the formula

$$\frac{6!}{3!(6 - 3)!}$$

which we solve as follows:

$$\frac{1 \cdot 2 \cdot 3 \cdot 4 \cdot 5 \cdot 6}{(1 \cdot 2 \cdot 3)(1 \cdot 2 \cdot 3)} = \frac{4 \cdot 5 \cdot 6}{1 \cdot 2 \cdot 3} = 20 \text{ different teams}$$

You may also notice that the factorial appears in the binomial theorem; study the theorem on page 207. Notice that the denominator of the coefficient of the fifth term is $2 \cdot 3 \cdot 4$, which is equivalent to $1 \cdot 2 \cdot 3 \cdot 4$, which is 4!. The denominator of any term k for $k > 1$ is $(k - 1)!$.

EXERCISES
6.5

1. How many different ways can you arrange the symbols $\triangle$, $\times$, 0 in a row? First write out the different ways, and then calculate how many there are by finding the value of 3!

2. Find the value of the denominator of the coefficient of the seventh term of the binomial theorem.

3. Find

   a. $\dfrac{9!}{6!}$ b. $\dfrac{(8!)(7 - 3)!}{(4!)(4!)}$ c. $(3!)!$

6.6   The Fundamental Theorem of Algebra

We found by expanding to the set of complex numbers that we could find a solution to a quadratic equation, such as $x^2 = 1$. We did not say, however, that solutions exist for all equations within the complex number system. At the age of 23, the great mathematician, Karl Gauss, proved that in the complex number system a solution exists to every polynomial equation in one variable with complex coefficients. His theorem is known as the *fundamental theorem of algebra*.

THEOREM 6-2 ──

Every polynomial equation of degree $n > 0$ with complex coefficients has a complex root.

──

The proof of this theorem is far beyond the scope of this text, but many other valuable theorems have been derived from the fundamental theorem. These include many with which you are familiar.

Theorem 1

If a polynomial $f(x)$ equals 0 and is of degree $n > 0$, then $f(x)$ has exactly n roots, or n linear factors whose product is $f(x)$.

For example, if

$$f(x) = x^2 + 3x + 2 = 0$$

then

$$f(x) = (x + 1)(x + 2) = 0$$
$$x = -1 \quad \text{or} \quad x = -2$$

Here $f(x)$ is of degree 2 and has two roots, or two factors, whose product is $f(x)$. (Remember that the real numbers are a subset of the complex numbers, and hence, according to the fundamental theorem, may be coefficients or roots.)

As another example, consider

$$x^2 + 1 = 0$$
$$(x + i)(x - i) = 0$$
$$x = -i \quad \text{or} \quad x = i$$

Again, we find two roots and two linear factors whose product is $x^2 + 1$.

Theorem 2

If a polynomial $f(x)$ equals 0 and is of degree n, then $f(x)$ may have fewer, but not more, than n distinct roots.

For example, if

$$f(x) = x^2 - 2x + 1 = 0$$

then

$$f(x) = (x - 1)(x - 1) = 0$$

and both roots are +1.

Consider

$$g(x) = x^3 - x^2 - x + 1 = 0$$

We note by inspection that $g(1) = 0$. Therefore we know that $(x - 1)$ is a factor of $g(x)$. From the definition of a factor, we know that $g(x) = (x - 1) \cdot h(x)$, where $h(x)$ is a polynomial of degree $(n - 1)$. You may recall from your earlier work the similarity between the division of polynomials and the division you did in grade school. Let us divide $g(x)$ by $(x - 1)$ and find $h(x)$.

$$
\begin{array}{r}
x^2 - 1 \\
x - 1 \overline{)\, x^3 - x^2 - x + 1} \\
\underline{x^3 - x^2} \\
-x + 1 \\
\underline{-x + 1}
\end{array}
$$

We can check our division, just as we do in arithmetic, by multiplying the divisor by the quotient to see if we obtain the dividend. Thus

$$(x - 1)(x^2 - 1) = x^3 - x^2 - x + 1$$

Since $h(x)$ is of degree 2, we know from Theorem 1 that it has two roots. We have found $h(x) = x^2 - 1$, and we see that it too can be factored. Thus, $(x + 1)(x - 1) = h(x)$. Hence, $g(x)$ has three roots as required by Theorem 1, but has only two distinct roots which is in accordance with Theorem 2.

Another important theorem is the fundamental theorem of arithmetic:

THEOREM 6-3 ────────────────────────────────

Any composite number (nonprime integers greater than 1) can be expressed as the product of a unique set of prime numbers.

──

For example, when we factored the number 538,461 (see page 19) into its *prime factorization* of $3 \cdot 3 \cdot 3 \cdot 7 \cdot 7 \cdot 11 \cdot 37$, the order of the factors in the set was immaterial because of the commutative property of multiplication. However, the set of factors is unique in that it is the *only* set of prime numbers whose product is 538,461.

Why is this called the "fundamental" theorem of arithmetic? What is the importance of being able to obtain unique sets of factors? We have always known, or suspected, that factoring is unique. Therefore it may seem trivial to call this theorem "fundamental." Sometimes the best way to appreciate the fundamental issue is to examine an exception to the case. We have always accepted "three times three" to be nine without much doubt—until we began operations in base 4, or 5, or 6. What would be our problem if we were working in a number system for which the fundamental theorem of arithmetic did not hold? Let us find out.

Suppose we use only the set of numbers

$$\{1, 4, 7, 10, 13, 16, 19, 22, 25, 28, \ldots\}$$

that is, the set of numbers generated by the function $q(x) = 3x + 1$, where x is any whole number. Now reduce $\frac{28}{100}$ to lowest terms.

If you proceed as in Chapter 1 by first reducing both the numerator and denominator to their prime factorizations you may find

$$\frac{28}{100} = \frac{4 \cdot 7}{10 \cdot 10}$$

According to our definition of primes, the fundamental theorem of arithmetic, and elementary number theory we now conclude that $\frac{28}{100}$ is in simplest form, since the prime factorizations yield sets with no common elements.

On the other hand, you may have found

$$\frac{28}{100} = \frac{4 \cdot 7}{4 \cdot 25} = \frac{7}{25}$$

Here we claim that the fraction $\frac{28}{100}$ is not reduced to its lowest terms, because both the numerator and denominator have the common factor 4. Note that we have a contradiction. We would be in even worse trouble if we began finding least common multiples of such fractions. The difficulty arises because the fundamental theorem of arithmetic does not hold in this system. We have lost the uniqueness of factorization, as illustrated by the two different sets of prime factors that we used for 100. That is,

$$100 = 10 \cdot 10 = 4 \cdot 25$$

The purpose of this brief arithmetical discussion was to emphasize the importance of the fundamental theorem of arithmetic. The theorem is easily stated, but its full impact is not so readily appreciated.

You should realize that a similar statement could be made about the fundamental theorem of algebra. The set of linear factors of a given polynomial are a unique set. Even more importantly, the fundamental theorem of algebra tells us that a solution exists in $C^\#$. Throughout our discussion, beginning with the counting numbers and ending with the complex numbers, we had to keep expanding our number system to obtain solutions to the equations we examined.

To solve $x + 5 = 3$ required the expansion of the counting numbers to I.

To solve $3x = 5$ required the expansion to Ra.

To solve $x^2 = 2$ required the expansion to R.

To solve $x^2 = -1$ required the expansion to $C^\#$.

But now the fundamental theorem of algebra assures us that we need no further expansion to solve *any* polynomial equation in one variable over the complex numbers; a solution exists and it is an element of $C^{\#}$.

EXERCISES
6.6

1. What value of x places the number 100 in the set of numbers generated by $q(x) = 3x + 1$ (x is a counting number).

2. a. List the first five primes in the set generated by $q(x)$.
   b. List the first four composite numbers in $q(x)$.

Completely factor the following polynomials by first dividing them by $(x - 1)$.

3. $x^3 + 2x^2 - x - 2$ 4. $x^3 - 7x + 6$

5. Using your results from problems 3 and 4, reduce the following expression to lowest terms.

$$\frac{(x^3 + 2x^2 - x - 2)(x^2 + x - 6)}{(x^3 - 7x + 6)(x + 2)}$$

SUMMARY

We have examined several interesting and valuable topics commonly found in traditional algebra texts. None of these topics was essential to the development of $C^{\#}$ in the preceding chapters, but they all have an important place within the structure of mathematics.

A brief review of modulo arithmetic helped us discover that the set of integers modulo n is a field if and only if n is a prime number. We also inferred that when n is a composite number, at least one of the field properties is not satisfied.

We learned that many mathematical systems are not fields and that many systems other than Ra, R, and $C^{\#}$ *are* fields. We found additive and multiplicative identities that were not 0 and 1. Yet regardless of the symbols used for the identities in a given field, the sum of an element and its additive inverse is always the additive identity; and the product of an element and its multiplicative identity is always the multiplicative identity. Similarly, the two operations of a given field need not be those we associate with the signs (·) and (+).

The absolute value concept was viewed as a rule or a function. Applications of the absolute value function were explored and some skill in its use was developed. As in past chapters, graphing again helped us achieve a more meaningful understanding of the discussion.

The binomial theorem was developed through the expansion of $(a + b)^n$. We found we could write any term of a given expansion, or the entire expansion, without performing any of the usual multiplication of polynomials. We noted the development and use of Pascal's triangle.

Factorial n was defined as the number obtained by multiplying all the factors 1 to n inclusive, with n greater than zero. The arbitrary additional definition for the special case of $n = 0$ was left to you to find and ponder. We noted the relationship of factorial n to the binomial theorem.

Work with a number system in which a composite number can be expressed as the product of more than one set of prime factors led to a better understanding of the fundamental theorem of arithmetic. This examination further helped us appreciate the importance of the fundamental theorem of algebra—a theorem easily stated, but not always fully appreciated.

CHAPTER REVIEW TEST

1. What is obtained in any given field when an element and its additive inverse are added?

2. What element of the set is obtained when an element is multiplied by its multiplicative inverse?

3. Show why I_6 is not a field.

4. Prove that I_3 is a field.

5. What is the absolute value of a negative real number x?

6. What is the difference in altitude between a point 100 feet below sea level and a point 5000 feet above sea level?

7. Find the solution set in I for the condition $|x + 2| < 4$.

8. Give a condition for which the following is the solution set in I: $\{-3, -2, -1, 0, 1, 2, 3\}$.

9. Tabulate the elements of the intersection of the set of integers and the set B, where $B = \{x \mid 3 > |3x - 4|\}$.

10. Sketch the graph for $y = |x - 3|$.

11. Sketch the graph for $x = |y| + 3$.

12. Use the binomial theorem to write the expansion of $(x - y)^5$.

13. Write the fifth term of the expansion of $(x + 5)^{11}$.

14. Write the row of numbers corresponding to $n = 11$ in Pascal's triangle. (See answer section for Exercises 6.4)

15. Find $(10! \div 9!) + 4!$.

16. Factorial n is defined in this text in terms of $n > 0$. How would you define factorial 0? Why would you do so? Can you find a definition for factorial 0 in another book?

17. Discuss the meaning and importance of the fundamental theorem of arithmetic.

18. Discuss the meaning and importance of the fundamental theorem of algebra.

CHECKING YOUR WORK

page 200
You probably found that the set is closed under both operations, that the associative and commutative properties hold, that multiplication distributes over addition, and that the additive identity is once again the element 0 and the multiplicative identity is 1. From

the table, we find that there is an additive inverse for each element in S. That is, for each element in S, there exists another element in S, which, when added to the first element, yields a sum of zero. Let us tabulate the inverse elements for multiplication. For each non-zero element of S, we must find a multiplier in S, such that the product is 1 — the multiplicative identity.

$$1 \otimes 1 = 1$$
$$2 \otimes \ ? = 1$$
$$3 \otimes 3 = 1$$

We find a multiplicative inverse for each nonzero element except 2. Since no multiplicative inverse exists for an element, the inverse law for multiplication is not satisfied. We must conclude that I_4 is not a field. This supports the generalized statement that I_n is a field only when n is prime.

Return to page 200

page 207

$$(a+b)^6 = a^6 + 6a^5b^1 + 15a^4b^2 + 20a^3b^3 + 15a^2b^4 + 6a^1b^5 + b^6$$
$$(a+b)^7 = a^7 + 7a^6b^1 + 21a^5b^2 + 35a^4b^3 + 35a^3b^4 + 21a^2b^5 + 7a^1b^6 + b^7$$

Note that the sum of the exponents of a and b in each term is always the same; it is always equal to n in the expansion of $(a+b)^n$.

Return to page 207

ANSWERS TO SELECTED EXERCISES

Chapter 1

EXERCISES
1.1

1. a. $\{2\}$ e. $\{0, 1, 2\}$
   b. $\varnothing$ f. $\{2, 5, 6\}$
   c. $\{0\}$ g. B
   d. $\{0, 1, 2, 5, 6\}$ h. $\varnothing$

2. a. $\{1\}$
   b. $\{2, 3, 4, \ldots\}$ or $\{x | x > 1\}$ or $\{x | x \geqq 2\}$

3. $AC, \quad BD, \quad BE, \quad CD, \quad CE, \quad DE$

4. a. F
   b. $\varnothing$
   c. $\varnothing$

5. $\{3, 5, 7, 9\}$

EXERCISES
1.2

1. $5(2 + 3) = 5 \cdot 2 + 5 \cdot 3$

3. $3 + 5 = 5 + 3$

4. $4 \cdot 6 = 6 \cdot 4$

6. Distributive property

8. Associative property of addition

EXERCISES
1.3

1. No, because $4 + 8 = 12$ and 12 is not an element of the set.

3. The set is not closed under addition or subtraction. The set is closed under multiplication and under division (except by zero).

5. $\{0\}$

EXERCISES
1.4

1. $\frac{23}{12}$ 3. $\frac{13}{14}$ 5. $\frac{18}{17}$ 7. $-\frac{7}{6}$

EXERCISES
1.6

1. $0.\overline{7} = \frac{7}{9}$

5. $0.91\overline{6} = \frac{11}{12}$

7. $0.375\overline{0} = \frac{3}{8}$

9. $0.4\overline{123} = \frac{1373}{3330}$

10. $0.\overline{285714} = \frac{2}{7}$

11. Yes, it is twice as much, but notice that the sequence of the digits is the same except that for $\frac{1}{7}$ we begin the series with the digit 1, while for $\frac{2}{7}$ we begin with the digit 2. Will this series be found for any number of sevenths, the only difference being the digit with which the series begins? Try it and see!

12. It's not impossible for you to do. Try it again until you get

$$N = \frac{(a_1 a_2 a_3 \cdots a_n \cdots a_m) - (a_1 a_2 a_3 \cdots a_n)}{10^m - 10^n}$$

Testing this formula with the problem $N = 0.4\overline{123}$ we find

$$N = \frac{4123 - 4}{10^4 - 10^1} = \frac{4119}{10,000 - 10} = \frac{4119}{9990} = \frac{1373}{3330}$$

EXERCISES
1.7

1. No, because $\sqrt{2} \cdot \sqrt{2} = 2$, which is not an element of *Irr*.

3. $C \subset I \subset Ra \subset R$ and $Irr \subset R$

5. Assume

$$a - \sqrt{b} = \frac{\sqrt{b}}{a}$$

$$a = \frac{\sqrt{b}}{a} - \sqrt{b} \qquad \text{(adding } \sqrt{b} \text{ to both sides)}$$

$$a = \sqrt{b} \cdot \left(\frac{1}{a} - 1\right) \qquad \text{(distributive property)}$$

$$\frac{a}{\left(\frac{1}{a} - 1\right)} = \sqrt{b}, \qquad a \neq 1 \qquad \text{(multiplicative inverse property)}$$

but the left-hand member of the last equation is a rational number because of closure under the indicated operations, and the right-hand member is an irrational number. This is a contradiction since Ra and Irr are disjoint sets. The proof is not yet complete because we excluded $a = 1$. The assumption can also be easily contradicted if $a = 1$. Can you show this?

EXERCISES 1.8

1. a. Transitive only
    c. Symmetric only
    e. None

2. Part f, "is the same age as," is an equivalence relation. It divides the original set into subsets of citizens of equal age. No citizen is in two different subsets. Every citizen is a member of a subset.

CHAPTER 1 REVIEW TEST

1. a. $\{0, 1\}$
    b. $\{0, 1, 2, 3\}$
    c. $\{\quad\}$ or $\varnothing$
    e. $D = \{-1, 0, 1, 2, 3, 4\}$,   so $D \cap B = \{-1, 0, 1\}$

5. No. For example:

$$8 \div (4 \div 2) \overset{?}{=} (8 \div 4) \div 2$$

$$8 \div 2 \overset{?}{=} 2 \div 2$$

$$4 \neq 1$$

6. b. It is *not reflexive:* one cannot be one's own sister.

    It is *not symmetric!* The second statement must be true for all cases where the first statement is true: that is, for every case where a is a sister of b it *must* follow that b is a sister of a. Consider the statement,

"Susie is a sister of Jim." Of course, it does not follow that "Jim is a sister of Susie."

It is *not transitive*. If Sue is Sally's sister and Sally is Sue's, then Sue is Sue's sister, but we have said this is not possible.

7. c. $-\frac{112}{15}$

8. If you cannot explain why you "turn it upside down and multiply," review what you know about reciprocals, or what you know about the division algorithm, or study a modern sixth-grade textbook. And if none of these do it—ask your instructor.

10. *Irr ∪ Ra*

11. b. $0.7\overline{3}$

12. $\frac{151}{165}$

13. By showing that the two numbers are relatively prime. In this case, 151 is a prime number, and it does not divide into 165 exactly. Therefore no common factor exists.

14. Since $ax < bx$, then

$$ax + k = bx \qquad k > 0 \quad \text{and} \quad x \ne 0$$

$$a + \frac{k}{x} = b \qquad x \ne 0 \qquad \text{(dividing by } x\text{)}$$

$$a + N = b \qquad N > 0 \qquad \text{(given } a < b\text{)}$$

Therefore,

$$\frac{k}{x} = N, \quad \text{or} \quad k = Nx, \quad \text{or} \quad x = \frac{k}{N}$$

and k and N are both positive so x is positive; $x > 0$, when $x \ne 0$.

But suppose x is 0, then $ax = 0$, $bx = 0$, and $ax = bx$, which is a contradiction of the given statement of $ax < bx$. So $x \ne 0$.

15. a. 20
    c. 48 yards
    d.

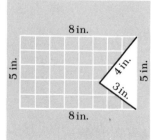

    e. 1 mile

f. To 100 add the product of the units digits, and to that sum add ten times the sum of the units digits.

$$17 \cdot 18 = 100 + 56 + 150 = 306$$

Chapter 2

**EXERCISES
2.2**

2. a. Quadrant I   e. Quadrant III
   c. Quadrant II   g. Quadrant I

**EXERCISES
2.3**

1. $x - y = 0$

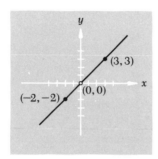

3. $x = y$

This is the same as problem 1 because

$$x = y \Rightarrow x - y = 0$$

5. $x - 2y = 4$ 7. $2x = y + 1$ or $2x - y = 1$

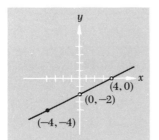

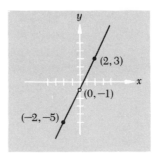

9. Two

10. As a check on the first two points plotted.

11. The point associated with zero degree longitude and zero degree latitude. This is the intersection of the equator and the prime meridian through Greenwich.

12. Ordinate

EXERCISES 2.4

1.–8. The equations of problems 6 and 8 are not linear.

9. $x = -4$: a vertical line through the point -4 on the x axis.
$y = 3$: a horizontal line through the point 3 on the y axis.
$y = 0$: the x axis.

EXERCISES 2.5

1. $x - y = 7$
$y = x - 7$
Slope $= \frac{1}{1} = 1$

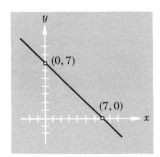

2. $y - x = 7$
$y = x + 7$
Slope $= \frac{1}{1} = 1$

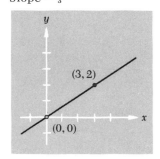

3. $7 - x = y$
$y = -x + 7$
Slope $= \frac{-1}{1} = -1$

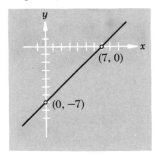

4. $2x - 3y = 0$
$y = \dfrac{2x}{3}$
Slope $= \frac{2}{3}$

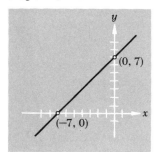

5. $y = 3x - 2$
   Slope $= \frac{3}{1} = 3$

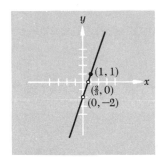

6. $y = 5$
   $y = 0x + 5$
   Slope $= 0$

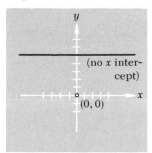

(no x inter-
cept)

7. $2x = 4y - 1$
   $4y = 2x + 1$
   $y = \frac{1}{2}x + \frac{1}{4}$
   Slope $= \frac{1}{2}$

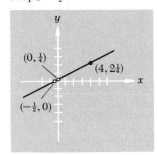

8. $5x - 2 = 3 - 6y$
   $6y = -5x + 5$
   $y = -\frac{5}{6}x + \frac{5}{6}$
   Slope $= -\frac{5}{6}$

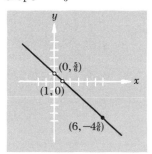

**EXERCISES
2.6**

1. $(0, 0)$; $(0, 0)$; $m = -3$

2. $\varnothing$; $(0, 3)$; $m = 0$

3. $(-4, 0)$; $(0, -2)$; $m = -\frac{1}{2}$

4. $(4, 0)$; $\varnothing$; m is indeterminable (that is, the line is vertical)

5. $(-\frac{7}{5}, 0)$; $(0, -\frac{7}{2})$; $m = -\frac{5}{2}$ 6. $(\frac{5}{3}, 0)$; $(0, -\frac{5}{4})$; $m = \frac{3}{4}$

8. a. $x - 2y = -11$ or $y = \frac{1}{2}x + \frac{11}{2}$
   b. $y = 4$
   c. $2x + y = -6$ or $y = -2x - 6$

9. $m = -2$

11. a. $y = -\frac{2}{3}x$ b. $x = -5$ c. $y = \frac{7}{3}x - 7$ d. $y = -6$

12. By noting the value of the ordinate at the point of intersection of the line and the y axis.

13. $k =$ the value of the ordinate of the y intercept.

**EXERCISES
2.7**

    1. $m = \frac{1}{3}$ 3. $m = -\frac{2}{5}$ 5. $m = 1$ 7. $m = 0$

CHAPTER 2 REVIEW TEST

    1. $m = 2$
        x intercept: $(-2, 0)$
        y intercept: $(0, 4)$

    3. $m = 1$
        x and y intercepts: $(0, 0)$

    5. $y = -4$, which is a line parallel to the x axis passing through the point $(0, -4)$.

    7. False

    9. True

  11. False

  13. $m = \dfrac{y - 5}{x}$, $x \neq 0$

        x intercept: $\left(-\dfrac{5}{m}, 0\right)$, $m \neq 0$

        y intercept: $(0, 5)$

Chapter 3

**EXERCISES
3.2**

    3. $12a^2$ 11. 0

    5. x^5 13. $(9ab^4 + b^3)/(a^3 - b^2)$

    7. $2^0 = 1$ 14. $3b + 6$

    9. $2a^2$ 15. $-16a^3 + 2$

**EXERCISES
3.3**

    7. Parabola

    9. Line

  11. Parabola

  13. Circle

EXERCISES
3.5

1. $x^2 + 6x - 27$
2. $x^2 + 3x - 10$
3. $x^2 - 11x + 28$
4. $x^2 + 10x + 25$

5. $6x^2 + x - 15$
6. $x^2y^2 - 49$
7. $x^4 + 2x^2y - 3y^2$
8. $x^3 + x^2 - 6x$

9. $(x + 4)(x + 7)$
10. $(x + 9)(x - 3)$
11. $(x - 5)(x + 4)$
12. $x(y + 2)(y + 1)$
13. $(2x + 1)(x + 3)$
14. $(3x - y)(2x + 3y)$

15. $(xy - 1)(xy - 6)$
16. $(3x - 4)(3x - 4)$
17. $(x + 9)(x - 7)$
18. $2ab(a - 7)(a + 5)$
19. $4(a - 9)(a + 2)$
20. $27ab(2a - b)$

21. $x = -3$, or $x = -2$
22. $x = 2$, or $x = 1$
23. The solution set SS is $\{5, 4\}$
24. $SS = \{-\frac{7}{2}, 6\}$

25. $SS = \{-3, 3\}$
26. $SS = \{\frac{1}{4}, 1\}$
27. $SS = \{0, 3\}$
28. $SS = \{15, 1\}$

EXERCISES
3.6

19. b. $\quad x$
$\qquad y$
$\quad x + \quad y$
$\quad x + \quad 2y$
$\quad 2x + \quad 3y$
$\quad 3x + \quad 5y$
$\quad 5x + \quad 8y$
$\quad 8x + 13y$
$\quad 13x + 21y$
$\quad 21x + 34y$
$\overline{\quad 55x + 88y} = 11(5x + 8y)$, which is the product of 11 and the seventh

term.

EXERCISES
3.7

3. $3x(x - 2)$
5. $(2x + 5)(2x - 5)$
7. $(a - 3c)^2$
9. $(3 - x)(y + 14)$

11. $(a + b)(a - b)(3x + y)$
12. $(x + y + 4z)(x + y - 4z)$
13. $(x^2 - 3y^3 + 10)(x^2 - 3y^3 - 10)$
14. $(a + b + c + 1)(a + b - c - 1)$

15. $SS = \{3, -2\}$
16. $SS = \{6, -6\}$
17. $SS = \{2, \frac{3}{2}\}$
18. $SS = \{4\}$
19. $SS = \{-2, y\}$
20. $SS = \{(y + 1), (y - 1)\}$

EXERCISES
3.8

1. $SS = \{-2, 4\}$ 7. $SS = \{-\frac{1}{2}, 9\}$

3. $SS = \{-5, 13\}$ 9. $SS = \{-\frac{2}{3}, \frac{1}{6}\}$

5. $SS = \{-7, 2\}$ 11. $SS = \{-\frac{1}{5}, \frac{1}{3}\}$

EXERCISES
3.9

1. $(x - 5)(x + 12)$

2. $(x + 6)(x - \frac{1}{2})$

3. $SS = \{-4, -20\}$

5. $SS = \{\frac{3}{2}\}$

7. $SS = \{-\frac{1}{3}, -\frac{7}{3}\}$

9. $SS = \left\{ \dfrac{3 + \sqrt{5}}{2}, \dfrac{3 - \sqrt{5}}{2} \right\}$

11. $SS = \left\{ \dfrac{\sqrt{2}}{2} \right\}$

13. $SS = \{2, 8\}$

CHAPTER 3 REVIEW TEST

1. $30 \cdot 6 = 180$

2. $200 \cdot 26 = 5200$

3. $(43 + 57)^2 = (100)^2 = 10{,}000$

4. $(8 + 12)^2 = (20)^2 = 400$;
   or $4(4^2 + 2 \cdot 24 + 6^2) = 4(4 + 6)^2 = 4 \cdot 10^2 = 400$

5. $4800 + 560 - 180 - 21 = 5159$

6. $10{,}000 + 600 - 16 = 10{,}584$

7. Assume it *is* true and arrive at a contradiction. For example, an irrational number shown equal to a rational number is a contradiction of the fact that *Irr* and *Ra* are disjoint. (If this hint is not enough, then repeat the same type of proof given in problem 8; you will arrive at the contradiction $2 = \frac{9}{2}$.)

8. Assume $\dfrac{\sqrt{a}}{b} = \sqrt{a} - b$,

   where $a, b \in R$, $b \neq 0$, and $\sqrt{a} \in Irr$

   $$\sqrt{a} = b\sqrt{a} - b^2 \qquad \text{(multiplying through by } b\text{)}$$

$$\sqrt{a} - b\sqrt{a} = -b^2$$
$$\sqrt{a}\,(1 - b) = -b^2 \qquad \text{(factoring)}$$
$$\sqrt{a} = \frac{-b^2}{1 - b} \qquad \text{(dividing by } (1 - b))$$
$$\sqrt{a} = \frac{b^2}{b - 1}$$

but this is a contradiction — no irrational can equal a rational number since $Irr \cap Ra = \emptyset$.

11. This equation is a quadratic because it is a second-degree polynomial in x.

17. b. $-4a^4$

22. $SS = \{2, -14\}$

28. y axis?   one time

x axis?   either two times, one time, or not at all

Chapter 4

EXERCISES
4.2

1. Examples of functions for the domain O and range E.

$$h(x) = x + 1, \qquad H(x) = 2x, \qquad g(x) = x^2 + x$$

Examples for the domain E and range O:

$$f(x) = x - 1, \qquad F(x) = x^2 + 2x + 1$$

2. $G(x) = x + 1, \qquad J(x) = x^2 + 2x + 1$

3. $y < 3x$

4. Figure 4-2; a many to one function. Why could the answer not be mapped here by the author?

5. $g(-5) = 45; \ g(-1) = 9; \ g(\tfrac{1}{2}) = 3\tfrac{3}{4}$

7. $D = r \cdot t$, and distance is a function of $r \cdot t$. Do you know why D cannot be the domain?

8. a. $N + 2$, where N is the first element.

EXERCISES
4.3

1. $SS = \{(0, 3)\}$

3. $SS = \{(-1, -1)\}$

5. $SS = \{(-1, 0), (2, 3)\}$

**EXERCISES
4.4**

1. Graphing

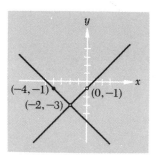

$(-4, -1)$
$(-2, -3)$
$(0, -1)$

Substituting (1) in (2)

$$(y + 1) + y = -5$$
$$2y + 1 = -5$$
$$2y = -6$$
$$y = -3$$
$$(1) \quad x = -3 + 1 = -2$$

Addition

$$x - y = 1$$
$$x + y = -5$$
$$2x = -4$$
$$x = -2$$
$$y = -3$$

3. By addition:
$$x - y = 1$$
$$3x + y = -3$$
$$4x = -2$$
$$x = -\tfrac{1}{2}$$
$$y = -\tfrac{3}{2}$$

5. The equations are equivalent.
SS $= \{(x, y)|3x - 4y = 20\}$

7. Solve both for y:
(1) $y = \tfrac{2}{3}x - 1$
(2) $y = \tfrac{2}{3}x + 4$
Both have the same slope.
SS $= \varnothing$

**EXERCISES
4.5**

1. a. Inconsistent
   c. Independent
   e. Dependent

2. a. The null set
   c. $\{(-2, -4)\}$
   e. $\{(x, y)|y = x - 2\}$

**EXERCISES
4.6**

1. $\{(-1, 2, 3)\}$

2. $\{(-2, 1, 3)\}$

5. $\{(2, 4, 0), (-3, -21, 30)\}$ (Did you find both triplets?)

**EXERCISES
4.7**

2. b. In the accompanying figure, the solution set of the system is the triple-hatched area in the form of a triangle and includes all points on the linear boundaries of this triangle in addition to all points within the triangle.

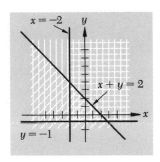

3. Study the accompanying figure. The cross-hatched area is the union of two conditions $x + y < 2.5$ and $x + y \geq 1.5$; therefore, it graphically illustrates the answer to the problem. These are the two conditions dictated, because regardless of the value of the real numbers x and y, their sum must round to the integer 2. Since 0.5 rounds upward, any value from 1.5 up to 2 rounds to 2; any value less than 2.5 down to 2 rounds to 2.

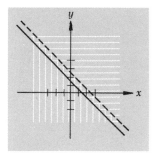

**EXERCISES
4.8**

1. The constraints can be reduced as follows, where x = wigs sold and y = wahms sold,

(a) $y \geq 4$ (we must produce at least 4 wahms to meet our contract)

(b) $y \leq 14$ (our machinery can produce only 14 saleable wahms daily)

(c) $x \leq 20$ (we can buy fewer, but no more than, 20 wags a day)

(d) $y \leq x$ (we produce and sell an equal number of wigs and wahms up through 14, and from there to 20 we sell fewer wahms than wigs)

These four constraints are plotted in the figure on page 230. Note that they form the polygon shown with the heaviest outline. We evaluate the four corners to find the minimum and maximum profit. Each point is determined by the system of simultaneous equations having the co-ordinates of the point as the unique member of their solution set.

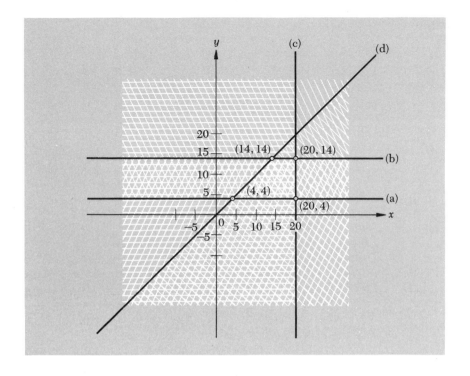

Point $(4, 4)$: Income = 4 wigs @ \$4 + 4 wahms @ \$3 = \$ 28.00
Costs = 4 wags @ \$5 = 20.00
Profit = \$ 8.00

Point $(20, 4)$: Income = $20 \cdot 4 + 4 \cdot 3 = 80 + 12$ = \$ 92.00
Costs = $20 \cdot 5$ = 100.00
Profit = (loss) \$ −8.00

Point $(20, 14)$: Income = $20 \cdot 4 + 14 \cdot 3 = 80 + 42$ = \$122.00
Costs = $20 \cdot 5$ = 100.00
Profit = \$ 22.00

Point $(14, 14)$: Income = $14 \cdot 4 + 14 \cdot 3 = 56 + 42$ = \$ 98.00
Costs = $14 \cdot 5$ = 70.00
Profit = \$ 28.00

Therefore, a procedure of buying 14 wags each day and producing and selling 14 wigs and 14 wahms yields the highest profit.

2.   The highest percentage-of-cost profit is achieved by keeping the sale of wigs and wahms equal—each of these being equal to the number of wags purchased. That is, the rate of production and sales indicated by the coordinates of any point on the line $y = x$ that is in the solution set of the system yields a maximum percentage-of-cost profit. Note this is 40% at both points $(4, 4)$, $(14, 14)$. Try $(10, 10)$.

CHAPTER 4 REVIEW TEST

2. y is a function of x

4. $x = -1$
   $y = 2$

6. SS $= \{37, 40\}$

8. bacon: 80¢ per pound
   butter: 40¢ per pound

10. SS $= \{1, -1, 0\}$

12. SS $= \{2, 0, -1\}$

14. SS $= \{(1, 1), (1, 2), (2, 2)\}$

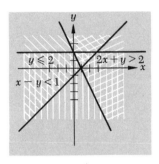

17. When $a > 0$

19. $-\dfrac{n}{2}$,   if n is even

    $\dfrac{n+1}{2}$,   if n is odd

Chapter 5

EXERCISES
5.1

1. Yes   7. Yes

3. Yes   9. It lacks the multiplicative inverse property.

5. No

EXERCISES
5.2

1. -1 5. -1

3. $-2i$ 7. $-i$

9. $-i = i^3$
$$= i^4 \cdot i^{-1}$$
$$= 1 \cdot i^{-1}$$
$$= i^{-1}$$

EXERCISES
5.4

1.	$10 + 6i$	11.	$13 + 34i$
3.	7	13.	$16 - 2i$
5.	$2 + 4i$	15.	$-13 + 26i$
7.	$-1 + 5i$	17.	$10 - 5i$
9.	$1 - 2i$	19.	$-30 + 10i$

21.	$27 - 2i$	24.	-26
22.	$-2 - 11i$	25.	$17 + 16i$
23.	-26	26.	2

EXERCISES
5.5

1.	$5i - 1$	7.	0
3.	2	9.	5
5.	$-2 + 46i$		

EXERCISES
5.7

1. This problem can be rewritten in terms of multiplication as:

$$(2 + 3i)(3 - 2i)^{-1} = (2 + 3i) \left(\frac{3}{3^2 + (-2)^2} + \frac{-(-2)}{3^2 + (-2)^2} i \right)$$

$$= (2 + 3i) \left(\frac{3}{9 + 4} + \frac{2i}{9 + 4} \right) = (2 + 3i) \left(\frac{3}{13} + \frac{2i}{13} \right) = (2 + 3i) \left(\frac{3 + 2i}{13} \right)$$

$$= \frac{6 + 13i + 6i^2}{13} = \frac{6 + 13i - 6}{13} = \frac{13i}{13} = i$$

Can we check this answer? According to our understanding of division, the product of the quotient and the divisor should be the dividend.
Check: $i(3 - 2i) = 3i - 2i^2 = 3i + 2 = 2 + 3i$

2. $$\frac{(4 + 5i) - (3 + i)}{2 + i} = \frac{1 + 4i}{2 + i} = (1 + 4i) \left(\frac{2}{5} + \frac{-1}{5} i \right)$$

$$= \frac{(1 + 4i)(2 - i)}{5} = \frac{(2 + 4) + (8 - 1)i}{5} = \frac{6 + 7i}{5} = \frac{6}{5} + \frac{7}{5} i$$

Check: $(2 + i) \dfrac{(6 + 7i)}{5} = \dfrac{(12 - 7) + (6 + 14)i}{5} = \dfrac{5 + 20i}{5} = 1 + 4i$

Also: $(1 + 4i) + (3 + i) = 4 + 5i$
Both the division and subtraction have been checked.

3. $\dfrac{i + 2(1 - i)}{i} = \dfrac{i + 2 - 2i}{i} = \dfrac{2 - i}{i}$

is really the expression we want to reduce. Let us find the answer in three different ways. First, because of closure under division, we know that $\dfrac{2 - i}{i}$ yields a complex number, which when multiplied by i gives the dividend of the original division problem $2 - i$. That is, $2 - i = (a + bi)i$. What can we place in the parenthesis for a and b to make this statement true? What times i gives 2? The answer must be $-2i$ for $i(-2i)$ gives $-2i^2 = 2$. Secondly, what times i gives $-i$? $(-1)i = -i$. So the answer must be $-1 - 2i$.

A second procedure might be to multiply the original problem by the multiplicative identity in the form of $\dfrac{i}{i}$ so as to obtain a real number in the denominator,

$$\frac{2 - i}{i} \cdot \frac{i}{i} = \frac{(2 - i)i}{i^2} = \frac{2i - i^2}{-1} = \frac{+1 + 2i}{-1} = -1 - 2i$$

The third procedure would be the straightforward application of the definition of the multiplicative inverse,

$$\frac{2 - i}{i} = (2 - i)(0 + i)^{-1} = (2 - i)\left(\frac{0}{0^2 + 1^2} + \frac{-1}{0^2 + 1^2}i\right)$$

$$= (2 - i)\left(0 + \frac{-1i}{1}\right) = (2 - i)(-i)$$

$$= -2i - i^2 = -2i + i^2 = -1 - 2i$$

5. $\dfrac{(x + 2i)(2 - i)}{3 + i} = 1$

Multiplying both sides by $\dfrac{3 + i}{2 - i}$, we obtain

$$x + 2i = \frac{3 + i}{2 - i} = (3 + i)\left(\frac{2}{4 + 1} + \frac{i}{5}\right)$$

$$= \frac{(3 + i)(2 + i)}{5} = \frac{6 + 5i - 1}{5} = \frac{5 + 5i}{5} = 1 + i$$

But if $x + 2i = 1 + i$, then $x = 1 + i - 2i$ or $x = 1 - i$.

Check: $\dfrac{(1 - i + 2i)(2 - i)}{3 + i} = \dfrac{(1 + i)(2 - i)}{3 + i} = \dfrac{2 + 1 + i}{3 + i} = \dfrac{3 + i}{3 + i} = 1.$

EXERCISES
5.8

1. $C^{\#} : x = \frac{1}{2}(1 \pm i\sqrt{3})$ 7. $R : x = 0, x = 1$

3. $R : x = \frac{1}{2}(1 \pm \sqrt{5})$ 9. $R : x = \frac{3}{2}$

5. $R : x = 1, x = \frac{1}{2}$ 10. $C^{\#} : x = \pm i$

**EXERCISES
5.9**

2. a. Quadrant IV   c. Quadrant III   e. Quadrant IV

**EXERCISES
5.11**

3. $\frac{14}{17} - \frac{5}{17}i$ 5. $\frac{27}{26} - \frac{5}{26}i$ 7. $\frac{1}{5} + \frac{2}{5}i$

CHAPTER 5 REVIEW TEST

1. $12 + 5i$

3. $-1 + 2i$

5. $1 - 3i$

7. $-\frac{5}{13} + \frac{12}{13}i$

9. $(3 + 2i) + (-4 + 3i) = -1 + 5i$

11. $i^{-1} = \frac{1}{i} = \frac{1}{i} \cdot \frac{i}{i} = \frac{i}{i^2} = \frac{i}{-1} = -i$

$i + (-i) = 0,$

so $-i$ is additive inverse of i

$(i)(-i) = -(i^2) = -(-1) = 1,$

so $-i$ is multiplicative inverse of i

13. $(a + bi)(c + di) = ac - bd + (bc + ad)i$
$= ca - db + (cb + da)i$
$= ca - db + (da + cb)i$
$= (c + di)(a + bi)$

15. $(a + bi)(c + di) = (ac - bd) + (bc + ad)i,$
but $(ac - bd)$ and $(bc + ad)$ are both elements of R, call them m and n.
Hence, $(a + bi)(c + di) = m + ni$, a unique element of $C^{\#}$.

17. $(a + bi) \div (c + di) = m \in R,$
when b and d are both 0 and $c \neq 0$ or when $a = c$ and $b = d$

19.   For any complex number $a + bi$, the complex conjugate is $a - bi$.

21. $C^{\#}$

23. $R, C^{\#}$

Chapter 6

EXERCISES
6.1

1.

$\oplus$	0	1	2	3	4	5	6
0	0	1	2	3	4	5	6
1	1	2	3	4	5	6	0
2	2	3	4	5	6	0	1
3	3	4	5	6	0	1	2
4	4	5	6	0	1	2	3
5	5	6	0	1	2	3	4
6	6	0	1	2	3	4	5

$\otimes$	0	1	2	3	4	5	6
0	0	0	0	0	0	0	0
1	0	1	2	3	4	5	6
2	0	2	4	6	1	3	5
3	0	3	6	2	5	1	4
4	0	4	1	5	2	6	3
5	0	5	3	1	6	4	2
6	0	6	5	4	3	2	1

The addition and multiplication tables for I_7.

2. a. From the tables we can tabulate:

$$x \# y = y \# x \qquad x * y = y * x$$
$$x \# z = z \# x \qquad x * z = z * x$$
$$y \# z = z \# y \qquad y * z = z * y$$

b. The identity for $\#$ is y because:

$$x \# y = x$$
$$y \# y = y$$
$$z \# y = z$$

c. The identity for $*$ is z because:

$$x * z = x$$
$$y * z = y$$
$$z * z = z$$

d. $(x * y) \# [z * (x \# y)] = y \# (z * x) = y \# x = x$

e. $(x * a) \# (x * z) = z * (x \# y)$
$(x * a) \# x = z * x$
$(x * a) \# x = x$
but $y \# x = x$
so $(x * a) = y$
hence $a = y$

f. $(y * z) \# 2 = x \# y \# z$
$y \# 2 = y$
$2 = y$

3. Yes, since we obtain:

$\oplus$	2	0	1
2	1	2	0
0	2	0	1
1	0	1	2

$\otimes$	2	0	1
2	1	0	2
0	0	0	0
1	2	0	1

and these can be rearranged in equivalent tables:

$\oplus$	0	1	2
0	0	1	2
1	1	2	0
2	2	0	1

$\otimes$	0	1	2
0	0	0	0
1	0	1	2
2	0	2	1

which are addition and multiplication tables for I_3.

EXERCISES
6.2

1. $\{-2, 2\}$

3. $\{-1, 0, 1\}$

5. $\{-2, -1, 0, 1, 2, 3, 4\}$

7. $\{\ldots -5, -4, 2, 3, 4 \ldots\}$ or $\{x \in I | -3 > x \text{ and } x > 1\}$

9. $\{-5, -4, -3, -2, -1, 0, 1, 2, 3\}$

11. $\{-4, 3\}$

12. $\{-8, -7, -6, 9, 10, 11\}$

13. $\{-1, 0, 1\}$

EXERCISES
6.3

5.

6, 7.

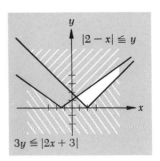

EXERCISES
6.4

1. $(a + b)^8 = a^8 + 8a^7b + 28a^6b^2 + 56a^5b^3$
$$+ 70a^4b^4 + 56a^3b^5 + 28a^2b^6 + 8ab^7 + b^8$$

3. $(3 + \frac{1}{4})^3 = 3^3 + 3 \cdot 3^2 \cdot \frac{1}{4} + 3 \cdot 3 \cdot (\frac{1}{4})^2 + (\frac{1}{4})^3 = 27 + \frac{27}{4} + \frac{9}{16} + \frac{1}{64} = 34\frac{21}{64}$

5. $\dfrac{12 \cdot 11 \cdot 10}{2 \cdot 3} a^9 b^3 = 220a^9 b^3$

6. $(3\frac{1}{4})^3 = (\frac{13}{4})^3 = \frac{2197}{64} = 34\frac{21}{64}$

   (Problems 3 and 6 illustrate two different ways of computing an arithmetic problem. Which method do you prefer?)

7. This triangle is known as *Pascal's triangle*. Blaise Pascal (1623–1662) lived in the great age of mathematics that produced Descartes, Fermat, and Wallis. Pascal was one of the many mathematicians with whom Fermat carried on a heavy correspondence. Pascal published many theorems without giving their proofs as a challenge to mathematicians of his day.

   The pattern used to determine the numbers in any row is to begin with 1; then each following number in the row is the sum of the two closest numbers in the row immediately above. Hence for the rows corresponding to $n = 9$ and $n = 10$ we build from the eighth row:

$n = 8$:		1	8	28	56	70	56	28	8	1	
$n = 9$:	1	9	36	84	126	126	84	36	9	1	
$n = 10$:	1	10	45	120	210	252	210	120	45	10	1

EXERCISES 6.5

1. Six ways:

   Δ   0   ×
   Δ   ×   0
   0   Δ   ×
   ×   Δ   0
   0   ×   Δ
   ×   0   Δ

   Computing: $3! = 1 \cdot 2 \cdot 3 = 6$ ways.

2. The denominator of the coefficient of the seventh term of the binomial theorem is equivalent to $6! = 720$.

3. a. $\dfrac{9!}{6!} = \dfrac{1 \cdot 2 \cdot 3 \cdot 4 \cdot 5 \cdot 6 \cdot 7 \cdot 8 \cdot 9}{1 \cdot 2 \cdot 3 \cdot 4 \cdot 5 \cdot 6} = 7 \cdot 8 \cdot 9 = 504$

   b. $\dfrac{(8!)(7-3)!}{(4!)(4!)} = \dfrac{(1 \cdot 2 \cdot 3 \cdot 4 \cdot 5 \cdot 6 \cdot 7 \cdot 8)(1 \cdot 2 \cdot 3 \cdot 4)}{(1 \cdot 2 \cdot 3 \cdot 4)(1 \cdot 2 \cdot 3 \cdot 4)} = 5 \cdot 6 \cdot 7 \cdot 8$
   $= 1680$

   c. $(3!)! = (1 \cdot 2 \cdot 3)! = (6)! = 6! = 720$

EXERCISES 6.6

1. 33, because $100 = 3(33) + 1$

2. a. 4, 7, 10, 13, 19, these numbers cannot be factored within the set $q(x)$.

    b. 16, 28, 40, 49

      That is,

$$4 \times 4 = 16$$
$$4 \times 7 = 28$$
$$4 \times 10 = 40$$
$$7 \times 7 = 49$$

3.

$$\begin{array}{r} x^2 + 3x + 2 \\ x - 1 \overline{\smash{\big)}\, x^3 + 2x^2 - x - 2} \\ \underline{x^3 - x^2} \\ 3x^2 - x - 2 \\ \underline{3x^2 - 3x} \\ 2x - 2 \\ \underline{2x - 2} \end{array}$$

$x^2 + 3x + 2 = (x + 2)(x + 1)$

Therefore

$x^3 + 2x^2 - x - 2$
$= (x - 1)(x + 2)(x + 1)$

4.

$$\begin{array}{r} x^2 + x - 6 \\ x - 1 \overline{\smash{\big)}\, x^3 - 7x + 6} \\ \underline{x^3 - x^2} \\ x^2 - 7x + 6 \\ \underline{x^2 - x} \\ -6x + 6 \\ \underline{-6x + 6} \end{array}$$

$x^2 + x - 6 = (x + 3)(x - 2)$

Hence

$x^3 - 7x + 6$
$= (x - 1)(x + 3)(x - 2)$

5.

$$\frac{(x^3 + 2x^2 - x - 2)(x^2 + x - 6)}{(x^3 - 7x + 6)(x + 2)}$$

$$= \frac{[(x - 1)(x + 2)(x + 1)][(x + 3)(x - 2)]}{[(x - 1)(x + 3)(x - 2)](x + 2)}$$

$$= \frac{(x - 1)(x + 2)(x + 1)(x + 3)(x - 2)}{(x - 1)(x + 2)(x + 3)(x - 2)}$$

$$= x + 1$$

CHAPTER 6 REVIEW TEST

    1. The additive identity

    3. We see from the table below that no multiplicative inverse exists for elements 2, 3, and 4 and that in several cases we lack uniqueness of multiplication.

$\otimes$	0	1	2	3	4	5
0	0	0	0	0	0	0
1	0	1	2	3	4	5
2	0	2	4	0	2	4
3	0	3	0	3	0	3
4	0	4	2	0	4	2
5	0	5	4	3	2	1

5. $-x$

7. $SS = \{-5, -4, -3, -2, -1, 0, 1\}$

9. $\{1, 2\}$

11.

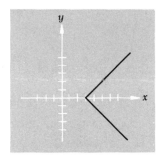

13. $330x^7(5)^4 = 206{,}250x^7$

15. 34

INDEX

A 8
B 9
C 0
D 1
E 2
F 3
G 4
H 5
I 6
J 7